European Construction

Macmillan Building and Surveying Series

Series Editor: Ivor H. Seeley

Emeritus Professor, Nottingham Trent University

European Construction

Procedures and techniques

B. Cooke

Principal Lecturer in Construction Management
Liverpool John Moores University

G. Walker

Senior Lecturer in Building Technology
Bolton Institute

MACMILLAN

690.094
C00

First published 1994 by
THE MACMILLAN PRESS LTD
Houndmills, Basingstoke, Hampshire RG21 2XS
and London
Companies and representatives   1091935X
throughout the world

ISBN 0-333-59465-7

A catalogue record for this book is available from the British Library

Printed in Hong Kong

Learning Resources
Centre

Series Standing Order
If you would like to receive future titles in this series as they are published, you can make use of our standing order facility. To place a standing order please contact your bookseller or, in case of difficulty, write to us at the address below with your name and address and the name of the series. Please state with which title you wish to begin your standing order. (If you live outside the United Kingdom we may not have the rights for your area, in which case we will forward your order to the publisher concerned.)

Customer Services Department, Macmillan Distribution Ltd
Houndmills, Basingstoke, Hampshire, RG21 2XS, England.

23.3.15

Contents

Preface

On 1 January 1993 the Single European Market came into being. This, amongst other things, marked the end of trade barriers and a relaxation of customs regulations, enabling free movement within the European Union.

J. Bloggs Ltd can start work on a project in Paris, with their workers catching the 05.30 train from London to Paris. Is this fiction or reality? It could prove to be a nightmare experience for many contractors hoping to make a quick profit (or even a loss) by joining the European bandwagon. A lot of hard lessons will have to be learnt.

How then will the professional building contractor, consultant or student, face up to the challenge? What will they need to know about the practices, procedures and construction techniques in any one or more of the European countries?

These are the questions which have prompted us to write this book. How can we as lecturers (often defined as the gatherers and distributors of misinformation) prepare our students for the European experience?

The only way forward was to go, see and record what was happening in Europe. This we have done in order to produce the core content for this book, which is based on personal observations of construction projects in The Netherlands, Denmark, France, Germany and Portugal.

The objectives were specifically to highlight within each country aspects of construction practices and building methods utilised under the following headings:

> Key information
> Construction output
> Review of the construction industry
> Extent of regionalisation
> The housebuilding industry
> Relationships within the construction industry
> The role of the Architect
> The role of the Engineer
> The role of the Quantity Surveyor
> Contractual arrangements and building procurement
> Planning and building control procedures
> Low rise housing construction
> Case studies on low rise housing projects
> Medium rise construction
> Case studies for medium rise construction

Within the text and diagrams an attempt has been made to bring out the differences in building from country to country. The construction details focus on the following building elements: foundations, external walls, floors and roof construction.

We hope that we have been successful in capturing the flavour of the countries visited.

B.C./G.W. April 1994

Acknowledgements

The authors wish to thank the many project teams who have allowed access to building projects in Denmark, France, Germany, The Netherlands and Portugal.

Special thanks are due to G. Dellaert, J. Maleyran, Professor A.C. Toepfer, J. Taylor, and J.U. Wolff for their hospitality when visiting the various countries.

The authors also thank Paul Hodgkinson for his assistance in the production of the drawings and Peter Williams for help with the section on procurement in the Introduction.

Professor I.H. Seeley has once again allowed us the benefit of his expert advice on the book content and encouraged us throughout. We also wish to express our gratitude to the publishers for their continual assistance through the production of the book.

Finally, we wish to thank J. Gunning, G.H. Yeadon and A. Hollway for giving advice on text corrections.

Lecturing materials available
A series of slide packs and a CD-ROM are available to aid lecturers on the subject of European construction studies. Details obtainable from: Brian Cooke, 82 Torkington Road, Hazel Grove, Stockport SK7 4RL (Tel: 061 483 6701)

1 Introduction to the European Union

1.1 Background

It is not the intention of this book to deal in great detail with the foundation and development of the European Union, its structure, Commission, Parliament or Courts of Justices. There are many books, commentaries and sources that specialise in these aspects, including the EU itself and the Government Departments of the Member States. However, this should not be neglected and broad overview is considered necessary to put the main content of the book into the European context.

The scene is perhaps best set by a quotation from Preamble to the European Coal and Steel Community Treaty of 1951:

> '...to substitute for age old rivalries the merging of essential interests; to create, by establishing an economic community, the basis for a broader and deeper community among peoples long divided by bloody conflicts; and to lay the foundations for institutions which will give directions to destiny henceforward shared.'

The integration of Europe into the Community as we know it today has grown out of the vision of such pioneers as Jean Monnet, Robert Schuman and Altiero Spinelli. The first initiative was the establishment of the European Coal and Steel Community (ECSC), known as the Treaty of Paris. The Treaty was signed in 1951 by six countries, Belgium, France, West Germany, Italy, Luxembourg, and the Netherlands. The intention was to rationalise the production of coal and steel (the strategic materials of war) in order to pre-empt another war between European states.

Further developments in the early 1950s led to the signing of the Treaty of Rome in 1957, which established the European Economic Community (EEC), an institutional structure to allow the six member states to co-operate as equals in setting common economic policies. The European Atomic Energy Community (EURATOM) was signed in the same year as a commitment to the safe development of nuclear energy in the ECC for peaceful purposes.

The UK unsuccessfully attempted to join the EEC in 1961 and 1967. In the meantime it joined with seven peripheral European states, not in the EEC, to form the European Free Trade Area (EFTA) which was only of limited success. The third attempt to join was successful and the UK became a member on 1 January 1973 along with Denmark and Ireland. The community of six had become a community of nine.

With hindsight, it can be said that remaining outside the community was a mistake for the UK. Trade with Europe had been growing whilst the trade links with traditional markets had been diminishing for many years. Only slowly was it realised that there was a need to be more closely involved with Europe.

It would be speculative to imagine that the impact the UK would have had on the initial establishment and development of the Community. However, it is easy to understand the friction and disputes that have arisen since membership was achieved in 1973. Instead of growing, evolving and taking an active role in the formation of the conditions and terms of the treaties, for the UK the 'rulebook' had already been written and had to be accepted.

The *Aquis Communicaire* (the body of law and practice) had been established by the original six nations and was not suited to the UK in some respects. This includes a major source of dispute - the Common Agricultural Policy (CAP), which was drawn up to suit the requirements of the founder states.

The first major test for the EEC came late in 1973 with the oil crisis and the consequent leap in the costs of energy. Although the cohesion of the Community was in danger of breaking, through the selfish reactions of individual states, the experience did much to strengthen the institutions within it.

The Community continued to expand during the 1980s, particularly in the south. Greece became a member in 1981, followed by Spain and Portugal in 1986, to bring the total up to twelve states. This has created an overall trading unit of in excess of 342 million people to compete with the USA (246 m) and Japan (122 m).

The following list sets out some key dates in the development of the European Union.

1947-1948	Benelux Customs Union	Luxembourg, Belgium, and the Netherlands
1948	Organisation for European Economic Co-operation (OEEC)	Co-ordination of post-war American aid to Europe
1949-1950	Council of Europe established	No real power but a forum to discuss issues
1951	European Coal and Steel Community (ECSC) The Treaty of Paris	France, Germany, Italy, Belgium, Luxembourg, the Netherlands
1957	The European Economic Community (EEC) and EURATOM - The Treaties of Rome	The six above signed for the establishment of common economic policies and safe development of nuclear energy for peaceful purposes
1960	European Free Trade Area (EFTA)	UK initiative with European States not members of the EEC
1961		UK applies to join the EEC - rejected
1962	The Common Agricultural Policy (CAP) is introduced	The source of many subsequent problems for the UK
1967		UK applies again to join the EEC - again rejected
1972-1973	Treaty on Accession of the UK, Ireland and Denmark signed (Brussels)	Norway was included but later withdrew
1974	Community Heads of State or Government establish the European Council	Decide to meet three time a year
1979	European Parliament	First direct elections held
1984	European Parliament	Second direct elections held
1986	Single European Act signed	To amend the Treaty of Rome to revitalise the process of integration between Member States
	Spain and Portugal join the Community	Now twelve States
1988	European Parliament	Third direct elections
	Berlin wall comes down	
1990	Germany is united	

1991	Agreement creating European Economic Area (EEA) signed	European Community and the EFTA countries
1992	The Treaty of European Union	The Maastricht Treaty
1993	The European Union (EU) comes into being	
1994	Austria, Sweden, Finland and Norway apply to join the Community	

Figures published in 1989 by the Commission of the European Communities (Eurostat) show that the Community is the world's biggest trading block, with 16.2% imports (USA, 15.5%, Japan, 7.0%) and 15% exports (USA, 12.0%, Japan, 9.1%). The Community is also the world leader in agricultural trade with 21% imports (USA, 7.0%, Japan, 8%) and 16% exports (USA, 15.6%, Canada, 2.6%).

The EU, in addition to being a fair trading partner, seeks to provide aid for the poorer countries of the world. Statistics from Eurostat show that the Community and Member States led the way in 1989 with $22 800 m dollars (Japan, $8949 m, other Western industrialised countries, $8000 m and the USA, $7659 m).

1.2 The Institutions of the European Union

The EU differs from other traditional international organisations in that it is a body founded in law. Member States when they join accept the Treaties of Paris and Rome along with a small loss of sovereignty to the independent institutions, representing national and shared interests, established within the Union.

The institutions cover the whole range of the EU activities and some knowledge and background of them is necessary in order to understand their roles, relationships and the decision making process.

The main institutions of the EU are:

> The Council of Ministers
> The European Council
> The European Commission
> The European Parliament
> The Courts of Justice
> Court of Auditors

1.2.1 *The Council of Ministers*

This is the main decision making institution. At any one time, it consists of a Minister from each Member State responsible for the policy area being discussed at a specific meeting, such as transportation, agriculture, energy, employment, etc.

In certain specified areas, such as fiscal matters and the Community Budget, the Council has joint control with the European Parliament.

The Council ratifies Community legislation in the form of:

Regulations - fully binding on all Member States.

Directives - as for a regulation but in terms of results, the means of achieving which are up to each Member State.

Decisions - may apply to one or more Member States in a way similar to regulations.

All draft legislation requires Council approval, usually by qualified majority. Only issues of fundamental importance, such as new policies, treaty amendments and the acceptance of new Member states, require unanimity.

Each state of the EU has a permanent representative, who has a staff of diplomats, based in Brussels. These representatives meet together to prepare the the agenda for meetings of the Council of Ministers, seeking to resolve potential problems of a technical or political nature. They are collectively known as the Committee of Permanent Representatives (COREPER).

An outline of the decision making process is illustrated diagrammatically in figure 1.1.

1.2.2 The European Council

The European Council is the title given to the regular meeting (at least twice a year) of the Heads of Government or State along with their Foreign Ministers. It should not be confused with the Council of Ministers. The European Council was only formalised by the Single Act of 1986. The idea had first been mooted in 1961 when with regular meetings it became clear that the important and complex issues facing the Member States required national leaders to discuss and decide upon them.

The European Council enables controversial matters, that have reached stalemate in the Council of Ministers, to be resolved, and it also decides and launches future policies. The EU, through European Political Cooperation (ECP), can react to international issues from a common standpoint. The President of the European Commission attends meetings of the European Council in his own right.

1.2.3 The European Commission

The Commission is a very important institution within the EU. It has 17 Commissioners (two each from France, Germany, Italy, Spain and the UK and one from each of the other seven Member States), who form a 'college'. Each Commissioner is appointed for a five year term by the Government of their Member State and is approved by the national Parliament. Each Commissioner pledges to serve the EC exclusively and not to take instructions from their national government or political party.

The President of the Commission is a Commissioner appointed to the office. The current President is Jacques Delors, first appointed in 1985, reappointed in 1989 and asked in 1993 to serve until 1995. The role of the President of the Commission is a key one and ranks with the Prime Ministers and Presidents of the Member States.

THE EUROPEAN COMMUNITY

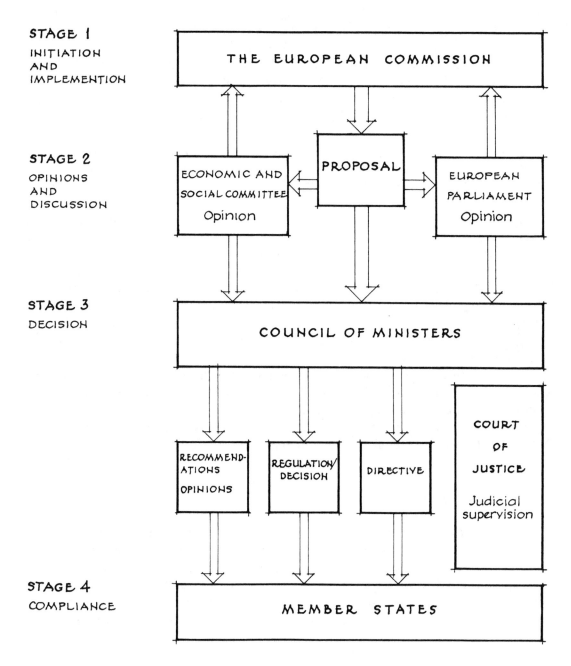

STAGE 1
INITIATION
AND
IMPLEMENTATION

THE EUROPEAN COMMISSION

STAGE 2
OPINIONS
AND
DISCUSSION

ECONOMIC AND SOCIAL COMMITTEE
Opinion

PROPOSAL

EUROPEAN PARLIAMENT
Opinion

STAGE 3
DECISION

COUNCIL OF MINISTERS

RECOMMEND-ATIONS OPINIONS

REGULATION/DECISION

DIRECTIVE

COURT OF JUSTICE
Judicial supervision

STAGE 4
COMPLIANCE

MEMBER STATES

DECISION MAKING PROCESS

Figure 1.1

All Commissioners have a policy portfolio for one or more of the Commission's twenty-three Directorates-General, and each is responsible for implementing common policies and general administration. The powers of the Commission are limited and defined by the initial Treaties establishing the European Community. It cannot determine future policies of the EU which are decided by European Council and Council of Ministers, although it can initiate new ideas. The function of the Commission can be set out under three headings, political, technical and judicial.

The **political** role of the Commission includes making policy proposals to the Council of Ministers which include major policy initiatives, draft recommendations on negotiating with countries outside the EU, EU research programmes and setting out preliminary draft budgets for the EU which must go forward to the Council of Ministers and the European Parliament for agreement.

The Commission negotiates with international organisations such as the GATT (General Agreement on Tariffs and Trade) and with other countries with whom the EU has economic relations, the USA, Japan, Central and Eastern Europe, as well as developing countries.

In its **technical** role the Commission manages EU policies such as funds for regional development, training and research. It also administers the CAP and has responsibility for programmes of assistance for developing countries, Central and Eastern Europe.

The **judicial** role of the Commission is essential and necessary if the EU is to operate successfully. As the Guardian of the Treaties, the Commission must ensure that regulations and directives adopted by the Council of ministers are properly implemented by the Member States. It must also ensure that measures, that would interfere with the free movement of goods, services, capital or people between Member States are not maintained or introduced.

The Commission must maintain fair competition and prevent inequitable practices that could undermine firms and jobs in other Member States, such as monopolies, cartels restrictive requirements and specifications.

The Commission can bring cases before the Court of Justice to enforce compliance of Member states with EU regulations and directives.

1.2.4 Court of Justice

The European Court of Justice is the supreme court and final arbiter in all matters of EU law. The Court, based in Luxembourg, comprises 13 judges, one from each Member State and chosen '...from persons whose independence is beyond doubt and who possesses the qualifications required for appointment to the highest judicial offices of their respective countries'. The judges are assisted by 6 advocates-general whose role is to analyse each case and draw up preliminary conclusions for the court but which are not binding upon the final judgement.

The Court is used to check that laws enacted by the Community are in accordance with the Treaties; these include disputes between EU institutions, governments of Member States or members of the public and EU institutions and action by EU institutions against a Member State.

The Court can be asked to give its opinion on the correct interpretation or validity of EU provisions by national courts.

Individuals, organisations and companies can appeal to the Court against EU decisions in such matters as unfair competition, where the Commission has established that certain practices are against EU rules. This type of case can be dealt with by a subsidiary court - the Court of First Instance, with the right of appeal to the European Court.

Many cases are referred to the European Court of Justice by courts and tribunals within Member states (called referrals) where the case involves aspects of EU law that are not clear. In this instance the Court's judgement is binding.

The judgement and interpretation of the Court thus becomes part of the legal framework of every Member State and helps to create a body of European law applicable throughout the EU.

1.2.5 The Court of Auditors

The Court of Auditors, a new institution under the Treaty of Maastricht, is appointed for a six year term by the Council. The role of the Court is to ensure that the financial affairs of the EU are properly conducted by checking that all the due revenues are received and that all incurred expenditure is lawful and regular. The Court of Auditors publishes an annual report at the end of the financial year.

1.2.6 The European Parliament

The European Parliament is not a law making body although it plays a significant part in the legislative process. The Parliament has 518 seats to which members are elected every 5 years.

Distribution of seats in the European Parliament (post 1994 in brackets)

France	81 (87)	Belgium	24 (25)
Germany	81 (99)	Greece	24 (25)
Italy	81 (87)	Portugal	24 (25)
UK	81 (87)	Denmark	16 (16)
Spain	60 (64)	Ireland	15 (15)
The Netherlands	25 (31)	Luxembourg	6 (6)

Since the reuniting of Germany 18 observers from the eastern Länder have been taking part in proceedings. At the time of writing four more countries have negotiated the first stages of Membership - Austria, Finland, Norway and Sweden. This will necessitate discussions and decisions on the number of seats in the European Parliament as well as having implications on the balance of voting.

The Parliament meets in plenary session in Strasbourg 12 times a year. The meetings of its 19 committees, which consider proposals in preparation for the plenary parliamentary sessions, are held in Brussels.

The Parliament, by helping to draft Directives and Regulations and putting forward amendments for the consideration by the Commission, shares in the legislative processes of the Community. More power has been given to the Parliament under the Treaty of Maastricht, which includes co-decision in matters connected with the free movement of workers, the single market, education, research, the environment, trans-european networks, health, culture and consumer protection.

If the majority of Members of the European Parliament (MEPs) are in agreement, the Parliament can stop the legislative process. The Single Act also requires that, in matters of international cooperation and association, agreements and future admissions to the Union must receive the approval of the Parliament. The Parliament can adopt or reject the budget put forward by the Council. When it does reject the budget, which it has done on two occasions, the whole process must start again.

Although MEPs are often frustrated by the Parliament not being the decision making body, it does provide a political thrust to the proceedings and its initiatives for new policies are frequently successful, as in the case of its draft Treaty on the European Union which was adopted in 1984, and the Intergovernmental Conferences on economic and monetary and political union.

1.3 The single market

The realisation that progress towards a single European market had been too slow and that too many barriers still existed prompted the 12 Members states to sign the Single European Act in 1986. The measures, over 280, seen as necessary to create the single market and provide greater competition were adopted by 1 January 1993.

Although there are some issues outstanding, the measures receiving adoption include:

- liberalisation of public procurement
- harmonisation of taxation
- liberalisation of capital market and financial services
- standardisation, harmonisation
- removal of technical and physical barriers and free movement of individuals
- harmonisation of company law on intellectual and industrial property to foster business co-operation

The Treaty of Maastricht, which came into effect on 1 January 1994, like the Single European Act, comprises amendments to the Treaty of Rome. It established the European Union (EU) which is supported by three 'pillars'. Firstly the European Community which includes all the major general matters concerning the EU, secondly Common Foreign Policy and Security Policy, and thirdly Interior Affairs, dealing with such matters as immigration and political asylum.

The Union is actively involved in other areas, developing policies running alongside the single market. It has a direct bearing on the lives of individuals as well as States and its influence is felt in such issues as environmental protection, health and safety, education, competition and consumer rights.

The Union seeks to keep Europe in the forefront of technological development. It encourages co-operation between the Member States in research projects and industrial applications, which includes electronics and computing.

The Union is seeking economic and monetary union as a means of establishing monetary stability in Europe encouraging growth and investment. Progress in political union and defence seeks to safeguard the values, interests and independence of the Union. More broadly, it seeks to promote international co-operation in the interests of peace and security within a framework of democratic rule of law, human rights and freedoms.

1.4 The European Union and the Construction Industry

1.4.1 Barriers to trade

Article 59 of the Treaty of Rome requires that the free movement of goods between Member States must not be prevented.

Article 7 prescribes that their populations must be free to offer their goods or services in other Member States without discrimination on grounds of nationality. The intention is to eliminate, so far as is practicable, unfair practices and barriers to trade. These requirements have a direct affect on the construction industry through Directives dealing with Public Procurement of goods and services and Construction Products.

Documents and standard specifications prescribing the use of material from a particular nation, specifying a particular trade name or product (except under very limited conditions), constitutes a barrier to trade.

Procurement procedures in the public sector should not restrict the use of products that comply with the safety and fitness for purpose provisions of the essential requirements.

1.4.2 Public procurement

The directives on public procurement are intended to achieve the objectives of the Treaty of Rome. The following directives have been adopted in connection with public works and supply contracts and have particular relevance to the construction industry:

Directive No.   Title and purpose

77/62/EEC   **The Supplies Directive and Amendments**
80/767/EEC   *Concerned with public supplies/products for the public sector.*
88/265/EEC

92/50/EEC   **The Services Directive**
Procurement of services by public bodies including maintenance and repair.

90/531/EEC   **The Utilities Directive**

93/38/EEC	*Covers the procurement of supplies and works contracts and private purchasers in the water, energy, transportation and telecommunications sectors (WETT).*
92/13/EEC	**The Utilities Remedies Directive** *This enables parties who have a grievance to seek redress when they consider that the Utilities Directive has been infringed.*
71/305/EEC 89/440/EEC	**The Works Directive and amendments** *Deals with procurement of public building and civil engineering works and certain contracts which may be funded up to 50% by public bodies.*

These directives are not intended to create a common public procurement procedure in the Member States, but simply to establish a basic set of common rules for projects above particular value thresholds.

The rules are concerned with issues such as the advertising of tendering opportunities, selection of contractors, the award of contracts and the notification of procedures, etc.

1.4.3 Competition

Under the EU competition law, Article 85 of the Treaty of Rome prohibits any arrangements which seek to limit or prevent trade between member states and this includes price fixing or co-ordination of competition arrangements. Exemption can be granted by the European Commission where it found that Article 85 is not applicable in particular circumstances or a **negative clearance** may be issued if the provisions are not being contravened. This was the case with the Channel Tunnel.

1.4.4 Value thresholds

The Works Directive (89/440/EEC) provides for competitive selective tendering. These requirements were enacted in the UK by the Public Works Contract Regulations 1991 which imposes additional criteria on tendering procedures. EU regulations require that contracts for works and supplies over certain value thresholds have to be advertised in the Official Journal of the European Community. This information is also available on a computer data base called TED (Tenders Electronic Daily).

The thresholds are shown below. It is a contravention of the directives to subdivide contracts into packages that are below the thresholds with the intention of avoiding compliance.

Contract	Threshold (ECU)
Public works	5 000 000
Public supplies	126 000
Public services	200 000
Utilities works	5 000 000
Utilities supplies	400 000
Utilities services	400 000

NB 5 million ECU is approximately £3.5 million

1.4.5 Tendering arrangements

The directives on public procurement provide for open, restricted and negotiated tendering arrangements. The procedures are self-explanatory and may be freely used under the Utilities Directive.

The Public Works Directive allows the use of restricted or negotiated procedures only in circumstances set out in the directive and which must be justified in writing.

In works and service contracts full information has to be prepared, in writing, setting out details of the contract, names of tenderers, reasons for selection and rejection, the name of the successful tenderer and the reasons why that tender was selected. This report has to be submitted to the EU if required. Unsuccessful tenderers are entitled to be informed of the reasons why their tender has been rejected within 15 days of the receipt of such a request.

Many public sector bodies in the UK have rigorous procedures to prevent collusive tendering and cartels and require tenderers to sign a collusive tendering declaration.

1.4.6 Tendering period

For each tendering procedure contracts are required to be advertised. This has to be done in the Official Journal of the European Communities (OJ) without any charge. As well as tender notices, contracting authorities are obliged to publish information on the proposed procurement programme and contract awards. This is to enable firms to identify suitable tendering opportunities and also to find out how the contract was actually awarded.

The requirements impose time constraints on the contracting authorities which may be different to the tendering periods that might be expected in their own member state.

For an open tender there must be a minimum of 52 days between sending the notice to the OJ and the date for receiving tenders. Where a preliminary notice is published the period becomes 36 days. For example, for a selective tender for a construction project over £3.5 million in value the following would apply.

Period for receiving requests to tender	36 days (min.)
Period for receipt of tenders	40 days (min.)*
Period for publication of award	48 days (max.) after contract award

* The contracting authority can, by publishing a preliminary or indicative notice, reduce this time allowance to 26 days.

1.4.7 Criteria for the award of a contract

Initially, tenderers must be deemed suitable for the award of the contract. Bankruptcy or non-payment of taxes may be reasons for being excluded, and balance sheets, references and details of previous contracts may be required.

Whilst competitive tendering is a fundamental principle of the European Union, the Directive on Public Works Contracts Regulations allows contracts to be placed on the basis of the lowest bid or that which offers the most economically advantageous solution. In this context, whole life costing tenders may be applicable for adoption into the public sector tendering arrangements, with some public authorities already moving in this direction.

The EU directives provide non-exhaustive criteria for deciding on the award of contracts. These typically include price, time and technical quality.

Low tenders cannot be rejected out of hand and the directives prescribe that enquiries have to be made to establish validity or otherwise of the tender. Calling for a priced bill of quantities may satisfy this requirement.

1.4.8 Construction Products

The Construction Products Directive (CPD), (89/106/EEC), was implemented on 27 December 1991. The main purpose of the Directive is to ensure that all qualifying construction products fulfil the Single European Market ideal and may be traded freely throughout the member states without technical, physical or fiscal restrictions.

The Directive describes a 'construction product' as 'any product which is produced for incorporation in a permanent manner in construction works'. To fall within the scope of the Directive a product must meet four criteria: it must be produced; placed upon the market; incorporated in a permanent manner in the works; and relate to at least one of the Essential Requirements.

1.4.8.1 Essential requirements

The CPD requires that construction products are fit for the purpose for which they are intended and that may satisfy national regulations. Six Essential Requirements are set out in the Directive. At least one of the Essential Requirements must apply to the product in use.

1. **Mechanical Resistance and Stability** - the construction works must sustain all the loading liable to act upon it without failure, excessive deflections or damage to other works, fittings or equipment.

2. **Safety in Case of Fire** - if fire breaks out the construction works must continue for a specific period of time, to support loads, limit the spread of fire or smoke within the works or to neighbouring works, whilst allowing occupants to escape or be rescued.

3. **Hygiene, Health and the Environment** - the construction work must not be a threat to the hygiene or health of the occupants or neighbours, which includes giving off toxic gas, presence of gas, radiation, pollution of water or soil, faulty elimination of waste, or the presence of damp, etc.

4. **Safety in Use** - the construction work should not present unacceptable risks of accidents in service or in operation such as slipping, falling, collision, burns, electrocution, or injury from explosion.

5. **Protection Against Noise** - the noise perceived by the occupants or people nearby will not threaten their health and will allow them to sleep, rest and work in satisfactory condition.

6. **Energy Economy and Heat Retention** - the construction work and its heating, cooling and ventilation installation should minimise the use of energy, depending upon climatic conditions of the location and the occupants.

1.4.8.2 Interpretation

The Essential Requirements do not contain sufficient detail for them to be applied directly and require further explanation. A set of six **'Interpretive Documents'** (IDs) is being produced to define accurately the content and intention of each Essential Requirement.

The IDs provide the link between the Essential Requirements that apply to the works and the need for standards that apply to the products. They are intended to classify product characteristics and establish a performance classification system along with technical bases, calculation methods and rules and a harmonised terminology. This is a necessary step for the production of harmonised standards. The IDs will be required primarily by the writers of standards and specifications and enforcement agencies rather than manufacturers and suppliers.

1.4.8.3 Standards

The European Committee for Normalisation (CEN) and the European Committee for Electromagnetic Normalisation (CENELEC) were established to co-ordinate all matters relating to standards at the European level and the development of *Harmonised European Standards*.

For the production of standards the CEN has Technical Committees for product areas. These in turn are sub-divided into Working Groups to deal with the different aspects of the product area. There is a further sub-division into Technical Groups who write the standards for individual products. Each group comprises representatives from all member states, a minimum of two technical representatives from industry and a spokesperson.

When the Essential Requirements have been applied to products and the standards have been produced, all the member states of the EU will be required to adopt them as replacements for the existing national standards. In view of the enormous numbers of products and existing standards which they are to replace it is likely that the process will take some considerable time.

Harmonised standards will be produced in three main types:

Category A standards -   standards of design, codes of practice, etc. for the whole works not single products, e.g. structural Eurocodes.

Category B standards -   these will be the specifications for materials and products

Category Bh standards -   these may apply across a wide range of products and will relate to testing methods, standards of measurement, etc.

Designers, manufacturers, contractors and users of products that come within the scope of the CPD will all need to be aware of the need to demonstrate Technical Compliance. The products will have to conform to a Harmonised Standard, a National Technical Specification or have a European Technical Approval. The CPD also refers to major or minor part products. There is a lack of a clear definition at this stage except that a major product requires full compliance whilst a minor product must meet Essential Requirements

A relevant *National Technical Specification* is an existing national specification recognised by the commission as complying with the Essential Requirements.

European Technical Approvals (ETAs) are product assessments, for fitness for intended use, carried out by bodies authorised for the purpose in individual Member States. Under this process new or innovatory products can be assessed under *European Technical Guidelines* for the award of an ETA. This is a similar process to that of Agrément certification.

When a product fully complies with the procedures set out diagrammatically in figure 1.2 it will be allowed to carry the CE Mark. This will not however be mandatory. The matter is the subject of another separate directive which is being drafted.

The CPD contains provisions for ensuring conformity with its requirements. These include powers of inspection, the role of enforcement officers (Trading Standards Officers in the UK) and the penalties (fines and imprisonment) for contravention of the regulations.

1.4.9 Eurocodes

The Directives outlined above - the Construction Products Directive, The Public Works and Services Directives, form the legal basis for the development of technical standards and harmonisation. The CEN Technical Committee 250 is producing a series of codes - Eurocodes - that will set out design rules and standards. Nine basic codes are envisaged. The codes will cover design criteria for most types of construction work and the structural materials used, including geotechnical works.

The codes are first published in the form of pre-standards (ENVs), which the BSI publish in the UK as National Application Documents (NADs). It is intended that ENVs should be used for the design of projects to provide feedback through the BSI to CEN for modifications, where necessary, to be incorporated into the finalised European Standard (EN).

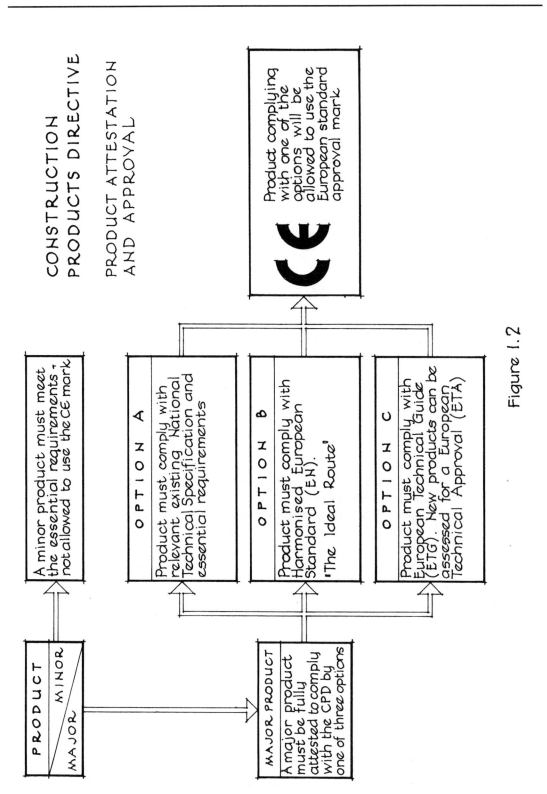

CONSTRUCTION
PRODUCTS DIRECTIVE

PRODUCT ATTESTATION
AND APPROVAL

Product complying with one of the options will be allowed to use the European standard approval mark

A minor product must meet the essential requirements - not allowed to use the CE mark

OPTION A

Product must comply with relevant existing National Technical Specification and essential requirements

OPTION B

Product must comply with Harmonised European Standard (EN). 'The Ideal Route'

OPTION C

Product must comply with European Technical Guide (ETG). New products can be assessed for a European Technical Approval (ETA)

PRODUCT

MINOR

MAJOR

MAJOR PRODUCT

A major product must be fully attested to comply with the CPD by one of three options

Figure 1.2

The following is a list of the proposed codes, each of which will divided into several component parts.

Eurocode No	Title	
EC1	Basis for design	ENV 1991
EC2	Concrete	ENV 1992
EC3	Steel	ENV 1993
EC4	Concrete and Steel Composite Construction	ENV 1994
EC5	Timber	ENV 1995
EC6	Masonry	ENV 1996
EC7	Geotechnical Design	ENV 1997
EC8	Earthquake Resistance	ENV 1998
EC9	Aluminium	ENV 1999

When the ENVs are ultimately finalised as fully agreed ENs, they will be transposed to replace the existing national standards of the Member States.

The Eurocodes will eventually be an essential part of the public procurement procedures. Their application should clear the acceptance of engineers designs between EU Member States as well as the EFTA countries who have shown a great interest in their development.

1.4.10 Mutual recognition

The Single European Act incorporates the essential right of people to move and work freely throughout the Member States. In order to make it easier for this to happen the Mutual Recognition Directives establish the system of recognition of professional qualification, professional education and training as well as experience.

Directive No.   Title and purpose

85/384/EEC   **The Architect Directive**
Concerned with mutual recognition of architectural qualifications by Member States.

89/48/EEC   **The First General Directive**
Sets out the means of mutual recognition of professional qualifications, higher education degrees and diplomas for the professions not covered by their own Directive.

92/51/EEC   **The Second General Directive**
Extends the system set out in 89/48/EEC for the recognition of qualifications gained from post-secondary courses and includes National

and Scottish Vocational Qualifications (N/SVQs) levels III and IV and awards from courses following a minimum school leaving age and experience. This Directive does not apply to occupations covered by their own Directives.

1.5 Conclusion

The purpose of this chapter has been to outline the general features of the EU and some of the main factors related to construction. There are many Directives that affect construction that have not been touched upon including those related to Health and Safety, Consumer Protection and others.

The reference and bibliography sections of this book lists many excellent texts and reference sources for readers who require more detailed information.

2 The Construction Industry in Denmark

2.1 Key information

Capital – Copenhagen
Area (sq.km)   43 075   Population 5.16 m (1992)

2.2 Construction output (1990)

Data obtained from the Euroconstruct Conference Report, June 1991

	ECU (Billion)
New residential construction	1.64
Private non-residential construction	1.54
(offices, industrial, commercial)	
Public non-residential construction	0.71
(school, universities, hospitals)	
New civil engineering works	2.79
Renovation in civil engineering	1.02
Renovation and modernisation in residential property	3.05
Non-residential renovation	2.11
Total	12.86

Current prices – 1 ECU = 7.87 Dkr (1990 average)

Building prices – labour and materials (January 1993)
The following data indicates key labour rates for labourers and craft operatives engaged
in the construction industry. A range of key material prices is also given in order that
comparisons may be made between each country discussed in the book.

Labour rate	Basic rate (per hour)		All-in-rate (per hour)
Unskilled labour	£11.00 (110 Dkr)		£21.20 (212 Dkr)
Craft operatives	£11.50 (115 Dkr)		£21.80 (218 Dkr)
Bricklayers	£11.90 (119 Dkr)		£22.70 (227 Dkr)

Material	Unit		Dkr	£
High yield steel – reinforcement	Tonne		8000	800
Structural steel	Tonne		6500-7000	650-700
Ordinary cement	Tonne		620	62
Carcasing timber	Cubic metre		2500	250
Clay bricks	1000		2700	270
100 mm Concrete blocks	Square metre		82	8.2
Social housing	Square metre (GFA)		10000	1000
Apartment	Square metre			
		Range Low	6500	650
		High	13000	1300
Factory units	Square metre			
		Range Low	2000	200
		High	3500	350

Value Added Tax rate (1993)   25% (all above rates exclude VAT)
GFA = Gross floor area
Data obtained from *Building*, 22 January 1993, Procurement – European Costings

2.3 Review of the Construction Industry

Construction output in Denmark in 1990 totalled around 12.86 billion ECU. Figure 2.1 illustrates the change in construction activity between 1986 and 1990. During this period the decline has mainly affected new construction. This has resulted in a change in the structure of production, with a higher proportion of work being undertaken in the building renovation and modernisation sector of the industry.

Construction activity in Denmark during the summer of 1992 was at an extreme low. The only major project being undertaken in Copenhagen at the time was the Tietgens Have Commercial project being constructed by Hojgaard and Schultz. The approximate project value was 220 million Dkr.

Construction Activity 1990
Construction Output 12·86 billion ECU

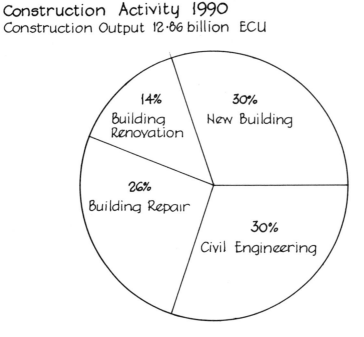

Construction Activity 1986
Construction output 14·2 billion ECU

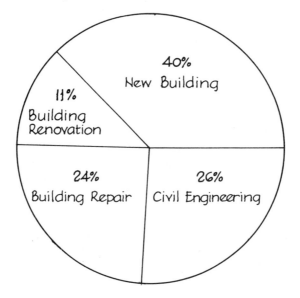

Figure 2.1

Major contracting organisations in Denmark include:

Rasmussen & Schiøtz	KKS Entreprise
Hojgaard & Schultz	KPC Byg
Monberg & Thorsen	CG Jensen
Phonix Contractors	Hoffmann & Sønner

The Store Baelt tunnel project and the Great Baelt bridge and tunnel project will aid the civil engineering sector for the next five-year period.

Between 1985 and 1990 housing starts have dropped by up to 10 000 dwellings per year. Excess capacity in the office and commercial property market has resulted in a sharp decline in the commercial sector.

2.4 Extent of regionalisation

Denmark is divided into three regions which include Jutland, North and South Zeeland and Funen. The regions are further divided into a number of local administrative authorities or councils.

2.5 The housebuilding industry

The housing market falls into three categories which include owner-occupied housing, subsidised housing and private rented housing. Subsidised accommodation may be constructed by housing co-operatives or local authorities. The percentage of home ownership in Denmark is approximately 60 per cent. Housing starts between 1960 and 1992 are shown on the histogram in figure 2.2.

The development of housing in Denmark relies upon close links between the building industry, researchers and the public sector. The general aim is to improve quality and productivity. A feature of housing development is the extensive application of pre-fabricated components to the construction process. Industrialised building results in reduced man hour consumption, improved speed of construction and an improvement in quality. This results in increased productivity and a more competitive industry.

The largest benefits are derived from developing buildings with simple geometric shapes. The aim is to create highly diverse building projects in which components from different manufacturers are brought together without any major effort.

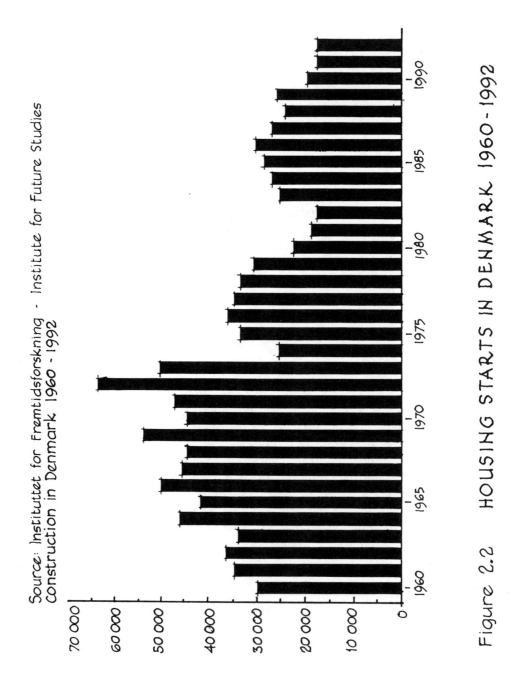

Source: Instituttet for Fremtidsforskning - Institute for Future Studies
Construction in Denmark 1960 - 1992

Figure 2.2   HOUSING STARTS IN DENMARK 1960 - 1992

Low/dense building with savings in resources

During the 1970s the interest in low density building projects became more pronounced often inspired by older Danish urban areas. The projects were aimed at saving resources in manpower and energy. They mainly consisted of small estates with from 50 to 100 dwellings with a variety of housing types. In connection with these 'green building projects' a number of experiments have been performed with the purpose of achieving savings in resources.

The Danish rules pertaining to experimental buildings are based on careful planning and subsequent evaluation of experiments carried out. Benefits from research are made available to the entire building sector in order to improve the whole building and living environment. The energy crisis of the 1970s stimulated widespread technological developments which led to a reduction of 50% of the energy consumption for heating and hot water purposes. This brought about the development of new insulation techniques, introduced a wide range of new materials and components and resulted in an increased awareness of the needs of building occupants.

Innovations included developments in solar heating systems and considerations for recycling waste products. As water prices rise and waste water treatment becomes more expensive a need has developed to recycle wastewater. Rainwater is collected from the roof and recycled with water from the shower in individual dwellings. The water collected is stored in a tank in the basement and is reused by pumping for toilet flushing within the building. The current aim is to obtain a 50% reduction in energy consumption by the end of this century, measured against the consumption in present day new construction. Danish environmental standards are high and aim to set the future standards for other EC countries to follow.

New high-flexibility housing – with increased productivity

In the 1990s the demand for increased productivity in building and construction is growing. Productivity growth may be achieved by an increase in the use of prefabricated components which can be easily transported to the construction site and fitted without further adjustment. Complete wall panels may incorporate all building finishes and services with connections to adjacent panels.

Buildings may be created which are so flexible as to encompass many different dwelling types and which permit regular alterations. An interest has developed in new building techniques for medium rise, multi-storey residential housing. The Sopheinborg Estate in Hillerd was built using light components. Load-bearing wall construction consists of steel components bolted together on site.

Facades, internal walls and floor components are of lightweight construction and were pre-assembled in the factory prior to fixing on site.

The Frederiksgade Project, outlined in section 2.15, is an example of a modular precast concrete framed building system for medium-rise housing. The wall frame system is based on the maximum standardisation of wall and floor components. Internal precast wall and ceiling surfaces are decorated direct. Internal floor finishes consist of hardwood strip floors laid on battens with service runs incorporated in the void space under the floor. The flats are heated by ducted air supplied from a district heating plant.

2.6 Relationships within the construction industry

The Danish construction industry operates in a similar way to that in the United Kingdom in that the architect undertakes the key role on behalf of the client. Figure 2.3 illustrates the contractual relationships between the parties involved in the social housing project. This arrangement may be used for housing schemes, refurbished works and small office projects up to the value of ten million kroner. As an alternative, trade contract arrangements, similar to the French *lots séparés* arrangement, may be used (see section 3.10.1). In this case either the architect or engineer may act as co-ordinator of the trade contractors.

For social housing projects tenders are obtained on an open tender basis, with contractors required to comply with certain tender qualifications. Large projects may be awarded by selective invitation to tender with 3 to 5 contractors bidding for the work.

2.7 Role of the architect

Architects undertake a theoretical study course of five and a half years duration at University. The courses are offered at the Danish Architectural Academy in Copenhagen or the University of Aarhus. Students entering university will normally have completed a three year grammar school education. These will be supported by mature students entering the course from Polytechnics.

The architect, during his course of study, may undertake a wide range of specialisms including historical renovation, architectural aspects of buildings, industrial design, interior design, landscape design and aspects of town planning. The activities of Danish architects in other countries are extensive. These include such buildings as the Sidney Opera House, the Saudi Arabian Foreign Ministry Building in Riyadh, and the triumphal Arch of Humanity, in Paris. In Danish architecture the emphasis is on functional suitability, proper use of building materials, simplicity of design and an approach that connects the architectural idea with the shaping of detail.

CONTRACTUAL RELATIONSHIPS – SOCIAL HOUSING PROJECT

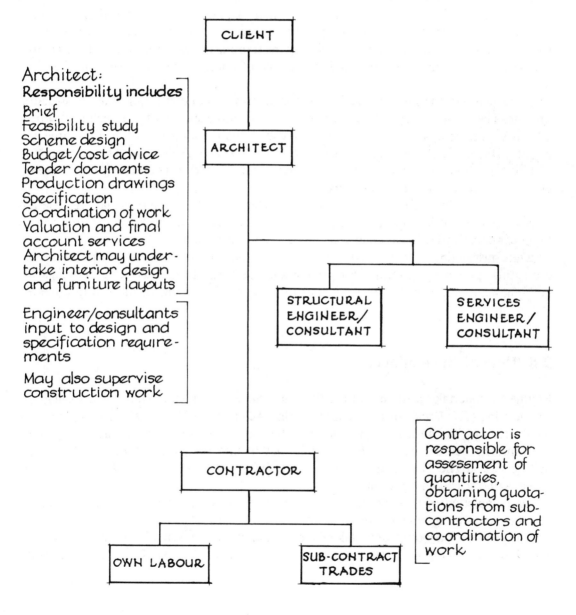

Architect:
Responsibility includes

Brief
Feasibility study
Scheme design
Budget/cost advice
Tender documents
Production drawings
Specification
Co-ordination of work
Valuation and final
account services
Architect may under-
take interior design
and furniture layouts

Engineer/consultants
input to design and
specification require-
ments

May also supervise
construction work

CLIENT

ARCHITECT

STRUCTURAL
ENGINEER/
CONSULTANT

SERVICES
ENGINEER/
CONSULTANT

CONTRACTOR

Contractor is
responsible for
assessment of
quantities,
obtaining quota-
tions from sub-
contractors and
co-ordination of
work

OWN LABOUR

SUB-CONTRACT
TRADES

Figure 2.3

Danish designers are admired for their furniture, lighting and electronics equipment, ranging from radio and television sets through to their ceramics and glassware.

The Danish Centre for Architecture and Building Export is located at Gammel Dok, in Copenhagen. This is a converted dockside warehouse built in 1882 which has been tastefully renovated to display the best Danish architecture. Regular exhibitions of Danish architecture and design are on display with occasional exhibitions on international architecture and construction.

Academic architects on completion of their degree course and training become members of the Architectural Academy (MAA). Figure 2.4 illustrates an overview of the technical and theoretical study periods during the training of academic architects, academic engineers and technical support staff in the role of constructing architects and building technicians.

Architects are assisted in practice by constructing architects within the construction process. The constructing architect first undertakes a three and a half year technical course after first practising as a craftsman or technician. This is followed by a further three and a half years of full-time study at a polytechnic (*Tekniske Højskola*). The constructing architect may obtain a position within an architectural practice, contracting organisation, engineers practice or public authority.

The constructing architect's undertakes the technical control, planning and organisation of construction work at the project level. They may also be engaged by the architect in the preparation of technical details and specification drafting.

The constructing architects course is broadly based and encompasses aspects of cost estimating, preparing quantities for pricing and the production of working drawings for building approval. The final year level of their course is the equivalent to a first degree in the UK.

2.8　Role of the engineer

Engineers undertake a three and a half year course of full-time study at a College of Engineering (*Teknikum*), or at The Engineering Academy of Denmark. On completion of the course they are awarded a first degree which allows them to practise as an engineer.

A masters degree course in Engineering may be undertaken over a period of five and half years at a The Technical University of Denmark (*Danmarks Tekniske Højskole*), or at the Aalborg University Centre.

On completion of their degree course, engineers gain employment with government agencies, consulting engineering practices and contractors.

The engineer may often undertake the role of client's representative on major building and civil engineering projects. Refer to the Teitgens Have case study in section 2.10.2.

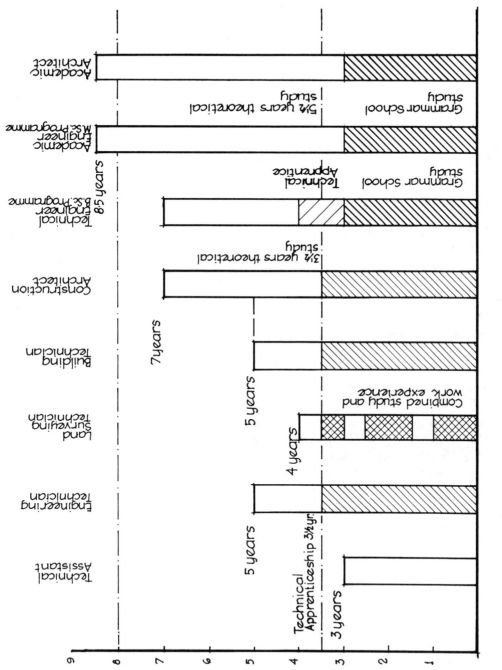

Figure 2.4 COMPARISON OF STUDY AND EDUCATIONAL REQUIREMENTS
FOR THE TRAINING OF ENGINEERS AND ARCHITECTS

2.9 Role of the quantity surveyor

The quantity surveying function is performed either by the architect or the consulting engineer as part of their professional services. The role of the quantity surveyor as a separate profession is unknown in Denmark.

The drafting of the specification and description of works to be carried out is prepared by the architect/engineer. The contractors undertaking the tendering process are responsible for the assessment of the quantities on which the tender sum is to be based. Building technicians and constructing architects may be employed by the contractor to undertake these roles.

The responsibility for the valuation of work in progress lies with the contractor. This is checked by the architect/engineer prior to payment by the client. Payment must be made by the client within *15 days* of the written payment request being submitted. Payment for work may also be based on stage completions in accordance with a payments schedule. The payment schedule must stipulate the date (time) stage, and the sum to be paid.

For building works the final account must be submitted to the employer within 25 working days of handing over the project. For major contracts this period is extended to 35 working days and for engineering works a 60-day period applies.

The general conditions for the provision of works and supplies within building and engineering are covered by Contract AB 92 issued by the Danish Ministry of housing (December 1992).

The AB 92 contract clauses are presented in a much simpler form than the JCT 80 contract and are more readable to the layman. The list of contents is:

Section   A – Contractual basis
             B – Performance bond and insurance
             C – Performance of the contract
             D – The employer's obligation to pay
             E – Extension of time limits and delay
             F – Handing over work
             G – Defects
             H – 1- and 5-year inspections
             I – Special provisions on defamation
             J – Disputes

Owing to the clarity of the general conditions there is not much scope for UK quantity surveyors to formulate a dispute.

An interesting aspect of the Danish contract is the requirement for a performance bond to cover 15% of the contract sum. This is reduced to 10% at the contract completion and to 2% after one year beyond the handover date. The process of applying a performance bond obviates the need for retention monies to be applied by the client.

2.10 Contractual arrangements and building procurement

The various methods of procuring construction work may be summarised as follows:

    a) Traditional contract arrangements
    b) Trade contract systems
    c) Design and build
    d) Project management arrangements

Traditional and trade contract arrangements have already been outlined in section 2.6.

2.10.1 Design and build

Design and build contractual arrangements are applicable to commercial projects, factory developments and public works contracts (the procurement of public buildings such as police stations, municipal buildings and offices).

Three to five contractors would be invited to tender for the project with three companies being shortlisted to submit schemes. A symbolic fee (to cover the costs of consultants in preparing schemes) may be offered by the client. Alternatively the no cure/no pay scheme may be applied.

Figure 2.5 illustrates the relationships on a design and build project, for an office block.

2.10.2 Project management

The CF Tietgens Have project is a large speculative commercial development in Copenhagen. The contractual arrangement for the project and the relationship between the design team is illustrated in figure 2.6. An overall perspective of the project is shown in figure 2.7.

The relationships on the project reflect a modern approach to a project management contractual arrangement. The project is under the direct control of a construction manager at site level who controls up to twenty work packages.

DESIGN AND BUILD ARRANGEMENT

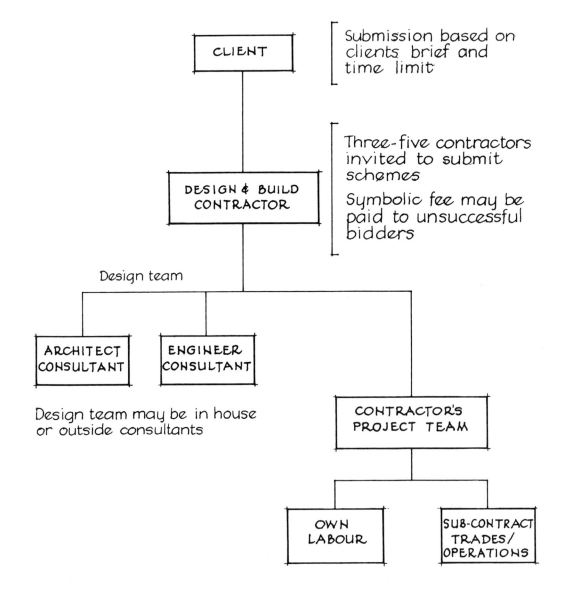

Figure 2.5

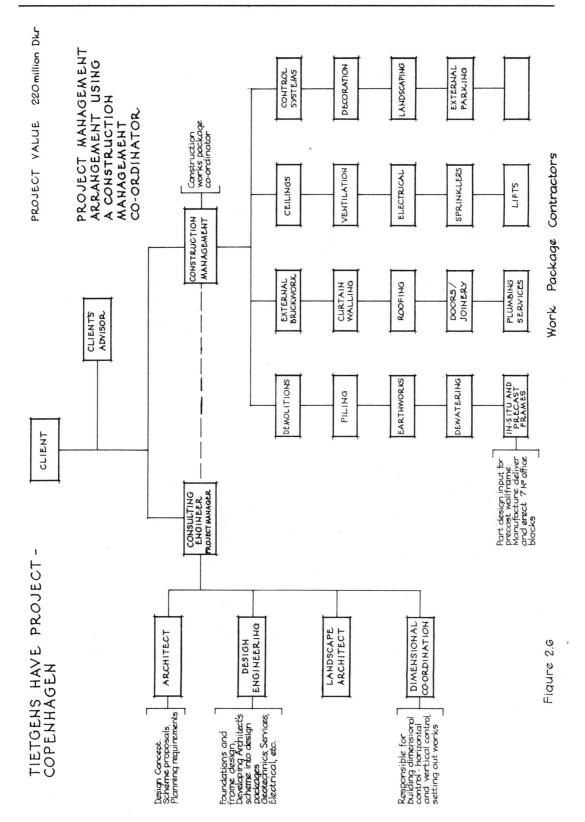

PROJECT VALUE 220 million Dkr

PROJECT MANAGEMENT ARRANGEMENT USING A CONSTRUCTION MANAGEMENT CO-ORDINATOR

TIETGENS HAVE PROJECT - COPENHAGEN

CLIENT

CLIENT'S ADVISOR

CONSTRUCTION MANAGEMENT

Construction works package co-ordinator

CONSULTING ENGINEER. PROJECT MANAGER

ARCHITECT
Design Concept. Scheme proposals. Planning requirements

DESIGN ENGINEERING
Foundations and frame design. Developing Architect's scheme into design packages. Geotechnics, Services, Electrical, etc.

LANDSCAPE ARCHITECT

DIMENSIONAL CO-ORDINATION
Responsible for building dimensional control - horizontal and vertical control, setting out works

Work Package Contractors

DEMOLITIONS
PILING
EARTHWORKS
DEWATERING
IN-SITU AND PRECAST FRAMES
Part design input for precast wallframe. Manufacture deliver and erect 7 Nº office blocks

EXTERNAL BRICKWORK
CURTAIN WALLING
ROOFING
DOORS / JOINERY
PLUMBING SERVICES

CEILINGS
VENTILATION
ELECTRICAL
SPRINKLERS
LIFTS

CONTROL SYSTEMS
DECORATION
LANDSCAPING
EXTERNAL PARKING

Figure 2.6

PROJECT MANAGEMENT ARRANGEMENT

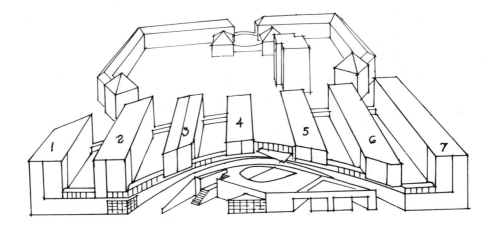

Block 1	3 450 m²
Block 2	4 100 m²
Block 3	2 650 m²
Block 4	1 500 m²
Block 5	1 740 m²
Block 6	3 200 m²
Block 7	5 160 m²

TIETGENS HAVE PROJECT

Figure 2.7

An interesting feature of the project is the use of a dimensional control consultant who is responsible for the setting-out procedures on site with regard to the horizontal and vertical alignment of the frame construction.

On the project the consulting engineer is acting in the role of the project manager and is responsible for co-ordinating design team information and liaison with the client.

A large number of work packages have a design responsibility. The concrete frame work packages include the design, precast manufacture and erection of the seven concrete structures. The frames are of load-bearing wall construction supporting twelve metre span floor units.

2.11 Planning and building control procedures

Planning and building control procedures follow a similar process to those undertaken in the UK. Planning and building regulations applications, however, are not subject to fees (other than a nominal fee to cover administrative charges). These include foundations, drainage, ground floor level and completion of the works. Building inspections are undertaken at four stages of construction by the authorities.

2.12 Low rise housing construction

Information collection

The case study material relates to a number of projects in the Horsens, Aarhus and Copenhagen areas of Denmark. Data relating to construction techniques has been obtained from visiting architectural practices and projects under construction. Information has also been obtained from manufacturers brochures and trade literature. The construction techniques outlined may not be typical of all building methods utilised in other regions of the country.

2.12.1 Museums of traditional buildings in Denmark

Visitors to Denmark who are interested in visiting 'old towns' (or an open air museum) should visit Den Gamle By, in Aarhus, Jutland, and the Frilandsmuseet Open Air Museum at Brede, near Lyngby, approximately 10 km north of Copenhagen.

Den Gamle By is a collection of some sixty typical old buildings that have been reconstructed to give the visitor an impression of an old Danish market town. The majority of the buildings originate from towns in Jutland, mainly from Aarhus and Aalborg. Other houses are from Funen and North and South Zeeland.

This museum has been accomplished partly through reconstructing original buildings from various Danish towns. It was opened in 1914 and now forms part of a private foundation, the aim of which is to show the development of civil life and trade in a Danish market town. The foundation has certainly achieved its objective. The Frilandsmuseet open air museum is located in 90 hectares of park land on the west bank of the River Molleaen, north of Copenhagen. The intention of the museum is to show country life in the period AD 1500-1800, especially by illustrating housing styles and living conditions in the different areas of Denmark. The houses – often doomed to demolition – have been measured and photographed and subsequently taken down piece by piece and then reassembled at the museum. The interiors of the houses are authentically furnished from the same period to help give the impression of country life. This is another essential visit for anybody interested in building conservation.

2.12.2 Form of construction

Current low-rise building techniques are mainly based on modular forms of construction. This may extend to the use of storey height lightweight concrete panels which may be used for internal or external wall construction. Traditional forms of construction may also involve the use of lightweight concrete blocks.

Danish building regulations require a high standard of insulation and the use of a 125 mm wide cavity completely filled with insulation is common practice. Externally the house may be finished in facing brickwork or rendered blockwork.

Internally the block walls or storey height partitions are plaster skimmed prior to decoration. Floors are screeded and finished with tiles, carpet or a timber strip floor on battens.

Roof construction is based on the use of prefabricated timber roof trusses covered with clay or concrete tiles. A layer of insulation 200 mm thick is incorporated within the roof space in order to provide the necessary degree of insulation.

2.12.3 Housing layout and design

Architecture is highly respected as an intellectual and artistic profession in Denmark. The architectural skills are very broadly based and architects are involved in many aspects of building and industrial design. This may range from planning new developments, interior design schemes, through to the design of furniture. It also may extend to other products outside the construction industry.

Danish housing designs are found to be rather unimaginative, boxey and over simplified. Designs vary from the simple gabled bungalow style as illustrated in figure 2.8, through to the modern three-bedroomed bungalow design shown in figure 2.9. Open ceiling features enhance the interior design and add a further dimension to the open plan interior layout.

Large sloping roofs are a feature of Danish housing design. This enables living or bedroom areas to be incorporated within the roof space and balcony features to be accommodated within the gable end.

A number of residential developments highlighted problems relating to flat roof failures. Danish architects and specifiers appear to have had suffered similar defect problems to those experienced in the UK with regard to flat roof construction.

2.13 Case studies in low rise housing construction

Figure 2.10 illustrates the North and South elevations of a modern single storey residential dwelling. The shallow pitched roof is finished with a PVC sheet membrane and incorporates a 200 mm insulation quilt within the ceiling space. Large roof overhangs are a feature of modern housing design.

Figure 2.11 illustrates a cross section through the external wall at the door and window openings showing the thermal insulation requirements to the floor, wall and ceiling areas.

2.13.1 Foundation and ground floor construction

Foundations for low rise dwellings consist of a simple strip foundation constructed of dense leca blocks or a reinforced concrete beam as shown in figure 2.12. Foundation insulation may be incorporated in the ground floor slab. Insulation may also be positioned down the inner face of the foundation in order to reduce the cold bridging effect to the surrounding ground.

Figures 2.13 and 2.14 illustrate the sequence of construction of the wall foundation and suspended ground slab. Insulation is extended one metre along the oversite concrete within the void area formed under the floor. Construction sequence directions are often included, alongside construction detail, to clarify the work sequences.

LOW RISE HOUSING DESIGNS

House I · Front and gable elevations

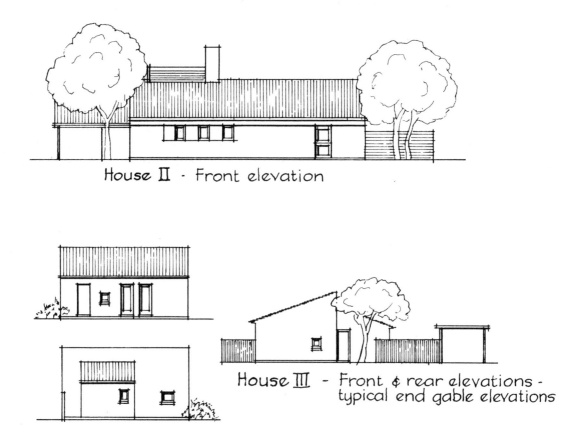

House II · Front elevation

House III — Front & rear elevations - typical end gable elevations

Figure 2.8

LOW RISE HOUSING DESIGNS

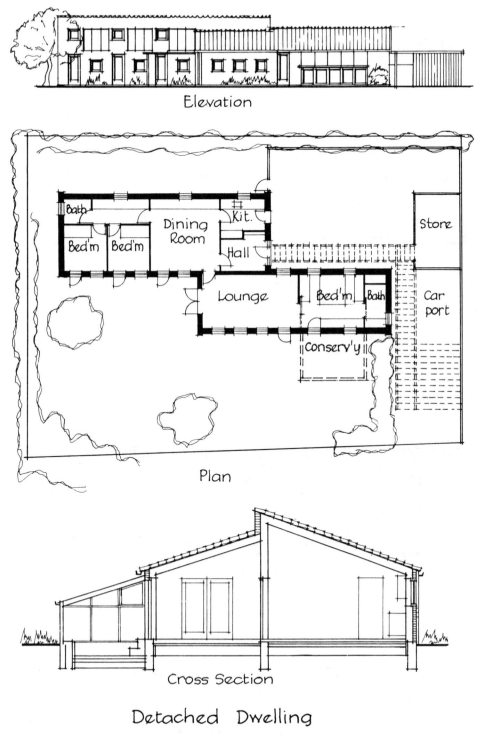

Elevation

Plan

Cross Section

Detached Dwelling

Figure 2.9

LOW RISE HOUSING DESIGNS

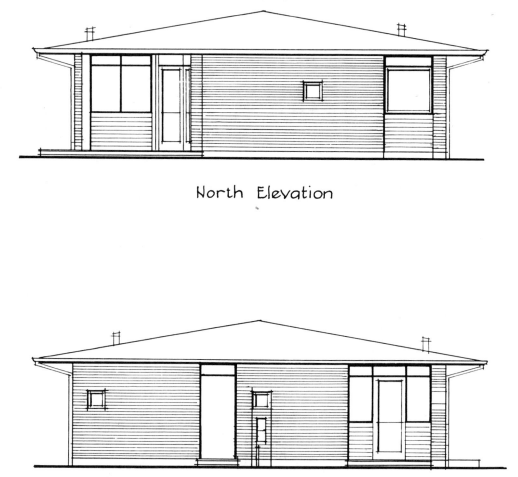

North Elevation

South Elevation

Modern design for low rise housing
in the Horsens region

Figure 2.10

EXTERNAL WALL CONSTRUCTION

Section at door opening

Section at window opening

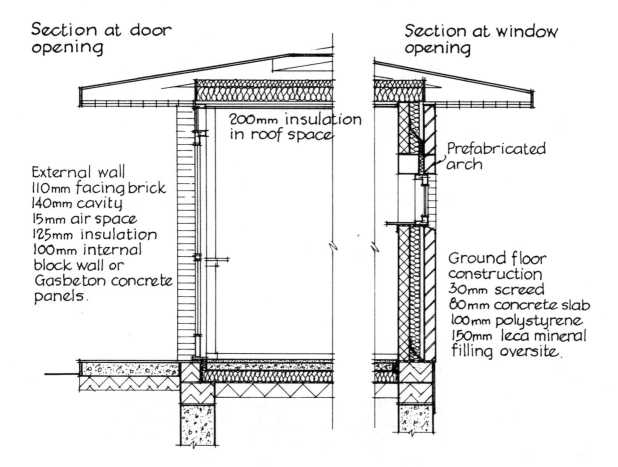

200mm insulation in roof space

Prefabricated arch

External wall
110mm facing brick
140mm cavity
15mm air space
125mm insulation
100mm internal
block wall or
Gasbeton concrete
panels.

Ground floor construction
30mm screed
80mm concrete slab
100mm polystyrene
150mm leca mineral
filling oversite.

Sections through external walls

Figure 2.11

FOUNDATION CONSTRUCTION

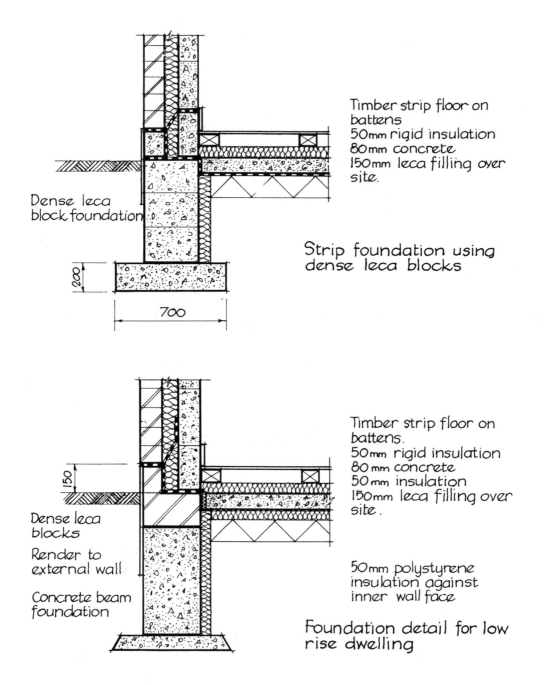

Timber strip floor on battens
50mm rigid insulation
80mm concrete
150mm leca filling over site.

Dense leca block foundation

Strip foundation using dense leca blocks

200

700

Timber strip floor on battens.
50mm rigid insulation
80mm concrete
50mm insulation
150mm leca filling over site.

Dense leca blocks

Render to external wall

Concrete beam foundation

50mm polystyrene insulation against inner wall face

Foundation detail for low rise dwelling

150

Figure 2.12

FOUNDATION CONSTRUCTION

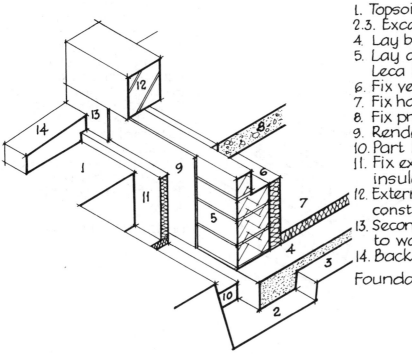

Sequence of work

1. Topsoil removal
2.3. Excavate foundation
4. Lay blinding
5. Lay dense block wall of Leca blocks
6. Fix vertical insulation
7. Fix horizontal insulation
8. Fix precast floor slab
9. Render to external wall
10. Part backfill
11. Fix external vertical insulation
12. External wall construction
13. Second layer of render to wall
14. Backfill to foundation

Foundation complete

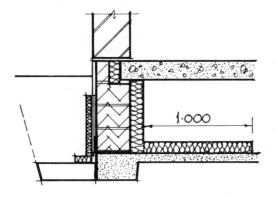

Precast concrete ground floor slab

Dense block foundation

Figure 2.13

FOUNDATION CONSTRUCTION

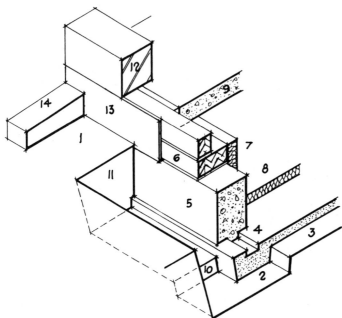

Sequence of work

1. Topsoil removal
2. 3. Excavate foundations
4. Lay blinding
5. Concrete ground beam
6. Laying of Leca blocks
7. Fix vertical insulation
8. Fix horizontal insulation
9. Fix precast floor slab
10. 11. Part backfill
12. External wall construction
13. Render to external wall below ground level
14. Backfill to site strip level

Foundation complete

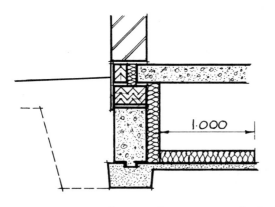

Precast concrete ground floor

Insitu concrete foundation beam

1.000

Section through suspended ground floor

Figure 2.14

2.13.2 Classes of foundation

Foundations are classified, for the purpose of meeting the requirements of the Code of Practice for foundation engineering (Danish standard 415), into three classes:

> Low foundation class
> Normal foundation class
> High foundation class.

When determining the foundation class for a project account has to be taken of:

> The nature and size of the structure
> The proximity of adjacent structures
> The soil conditions
> Ground water conditions.

Low foundation class foundations are suitable for small and relatively simple structures such as domestic dwellings and light buildings. Maximum design loads of 250 N/metre are suitable for spread or strip footings and continuous footings and may accommodate loads up to 100 N/metre run. Low class foundations will satisfy the majority of low rise buildings. Foundations of low class types are not suitable for excavation below the ground water table.

Normal foundation class – this class includes structures for which it is necessary to use geotechnical data to ensure that functional requirements are complied with. Structures assigned to normal foundations are raft type foundations and continuous reinforced concrete strip foundations.

2.13.3 External wall construction

Figure 2.15 illustrates the the front and rear elevations of a two-storey block of flats on a social housing project. A section through the external wall and floor construction is illustrated in figure 2.16. Details of the insulation requirements to the external walls are indicated for the walls, floor and roof elements.

EXTERNAL WALL CONSTRUCTION

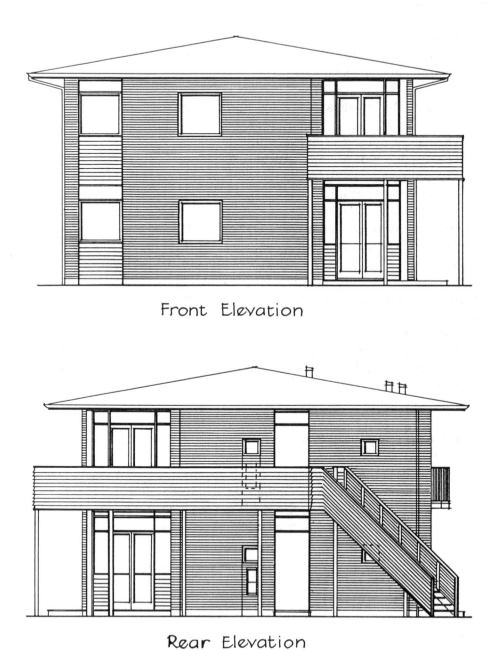

Front Elevation

Rear Elevation

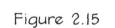

Figure 2.15

EXTERNAL WALL CONSTRUCTION

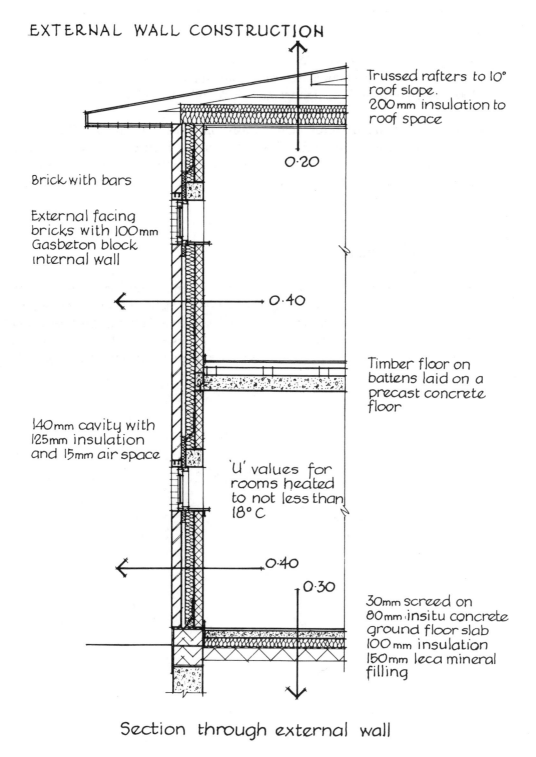

Trussed rafters to 10°
roof slope.
200 mm insulation to
roof space

Brick with bars

External facing
bricks with 100 mm
Gasbeton block
internal wall

0·20

0·40

Timber floor on
battens laid on a
precast concrete
floor

140 mm cavity with
125 mm insulation
and 15 mm air space

'U' values for
rooms heated
to not less than
18° C

0·40

0·30

30 mm screed on
80 mm insitu concrete
ground floor slab
100 mm insulation
150 mm leca mineral
filling

Section through external wall

Figure 2.16

External wall construction may be formed using traditional construction methods consisting of:

> 110 mm External facing brick
> 140 mm Cavity, containing 125 mm insulation and 15 mm air space
> 100 mm Internal wall of lightweight blocks (Gasbeton blocks).

As an alternative, modular storey height Gasbeton panels may be specified for the internal walls and rendered blockwork utilised externally. Figure 2.16 indicates a full height section through the external wall showing full cavity insulation. Figure 2.17 illustrates alternative external wall construction and sill details showing the positioning of damp-proof courses and insulation.

2.13.4 *Roof construction*

Figure 2.18 illustrates construction details of a trussed rafter suitable for a domestic roof. The trusses are fixed at 600 mm centres and incorporate an inclined ceiling finished with plasterboard. The roof space incorporates a layer of insulation 200 mm thickness. Roof finishes consist of clay or concrete roof tiles. For the shallower roof slopes finishes may consist of a range of felted finishes or patent PVCu roofing systems incorporating sealed joints.

EXTERNAL WALL CONSTRUCTION

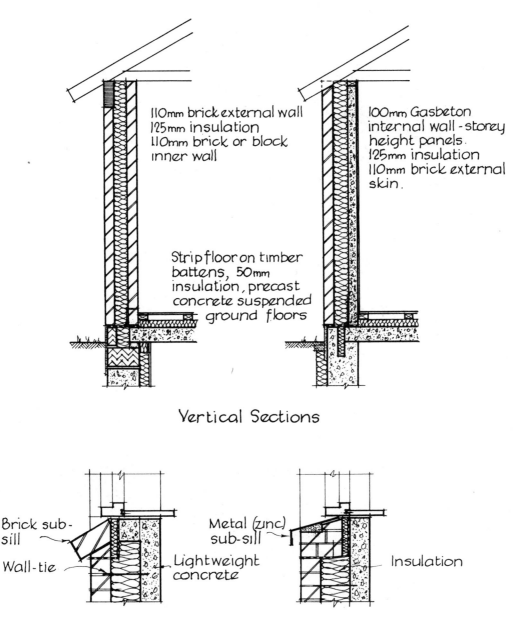

110mm brick external wall
125mm insulation
110mm brick or block inner wall

100mm Gasbeton internal wall - storey height panels.
125mm insulation
110mm brick external skin.

Strip floor on timber battens, 50mm insulation, precast concrete suspended ground floors

Vertical Sections

Brick sub-sill

Wall-tie

Metal (zinc) sub-sill

Lightweight concrete

Insulation

Typical Sill Details

Figure 2.17

ROOF CONSTRUCTION

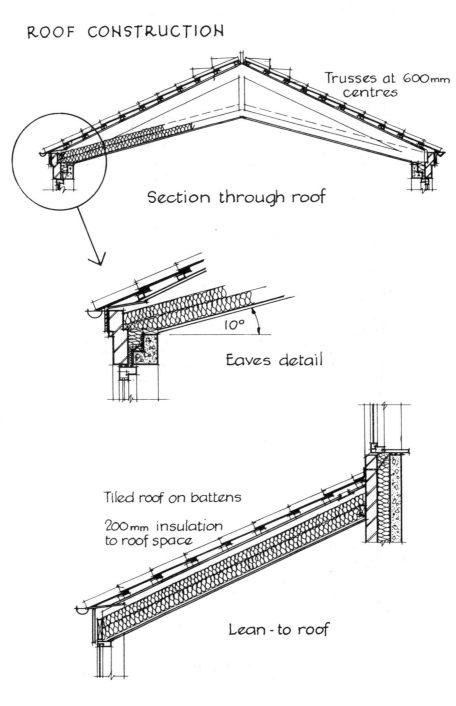

Trusses at 600mm
centres

Section through roof

10°

Eaves detail

Tiled roof on battens

200mm insulation
to roof space

Lean-to roof

Figure 2.18

2.13.5 *Thermal insulation requirements*

The thermal insulation requirements are presented in tabular form in figure 2.19. U-value requirements are relative to the internal room temperature and the total weight of the external wall element. Figure 2.20 illustrates the thermal requirements for the walls, floor and roof elements relative to the temperature and wall weight.

	Rooms heated to not less than 10°C	Rooms heated to not less than 18°C
External wall Total weight exceeding 100 kg/m² Total weight less than 100 kg/m²	0.60 0.45	0.40 0.30
Ground floor Solid ground floor Floor over a ventilated crawlway	0.45 0.45	0.30 0.30
Suspended floor Floor above the external air Floor/ceiling adjacent to a room heated to more than 10°C	0.30 0.60	0.20 0.40
Ceiling and roof structures Ceilings and roof structures adjacent to unheated roof spaces	0.40	0.20

Figure 2.19

2.13.6 *Low rise housing case study using the Gasbeton panel system*

The Gasbeton panel system incorporates 100 mm thick storey height panels to form the internal enclosure of the building. The 600 mm wide panels are adhesive jointed and incorporate thickenings at the door and window openings.

THERMAL INSULATION REQUIREMENTS ('U' VALUES)

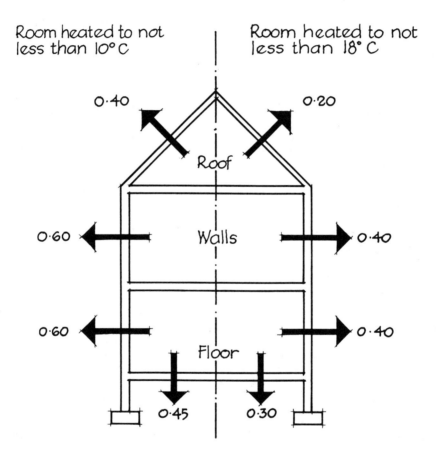

Room heated to not less than 10°C

Room heated to not less than 18°C

0·40 — Roof — 0·20

0·60 — Walls — 0·40

0·60 — — 0·40

Floor

0·45 — — 0·30

Situation for external wall construction not exceeding a weight of 100 Kg/m²

Figure 2.20

2.13.7 Sequence of construction

Figure 2.21 indicates a layout plan showing the location of the 600 mm wide storey height panels. Make up panels are incorporated to accommodate the room sizes.
A section through the external wall construction is shown which is built up as follows:

> 110 mm facing brick externally
> 125 mm full cavity insulation
> 100 mm internal Gasbeton panel.

Figures 2.22 and 2.23 illustrate the sequence of construction in stages 1 to 9. Figure 2.24 indicates a section through the external wall below sill level showing the insulation and the damp course requirements. Metal straps are inserted within the cavity wall to provide a tie or strap fixing to the roof. Figure 2.25 shows the positioning of the timber roof trusses which are finished with clay or concrete tiles.

2.14 Medium rise housing

Medium rise construction relates to building over two storeys in height but not exceeding nine storeys. In the majority of cases this relates to multi-storey flat construction. The National Building Code of 1960 contained provisions aimed directly at providing an increase in production. The code promoted the modular approach to the construction process.

2.14.1 The Danish approach to modular systems of building

The principles of modular systems were established in the Montagebyggeri reference published in the early 1960s. The modular system is aimed at achieving the following advantages for the building industry:

1. DIMENSIONAL CO-ORDINATION was introduced for the purpose of simplification and clarification.
2. LIMITATION OF VARIANTS in respect of dimensions that need not differ which assist in promoting
3. STANDARDISATION of building components and structures, thus permitting
4. PREFABRICATION of an increasing number of building components, so that
5. INDUSTRIALISATION of the building process can continue to widen the scope.

GASBETON LIGHTWEIGHT PANEL SYSTEM FOR LOW RISE HOUSING

Internal wall panel system

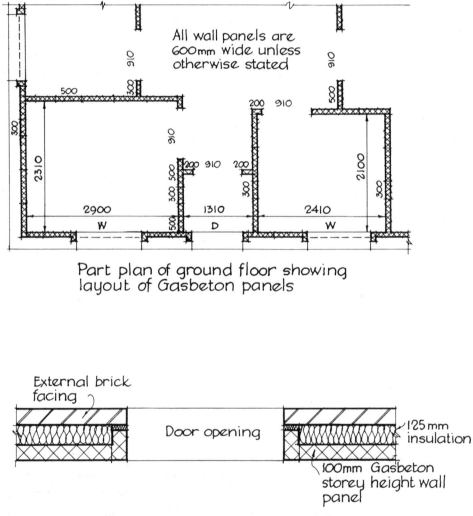

All wall panels are 600mm wide unless otherwise stated

Part plan of ground floor showing layout of Gasbeton panels

External brick facing

Door opening

125 mm insulation

100mm Gasbeton storey height wall panel

Section through external wall

Figure 2.21

GASBETON LIGHTWEIGHT PANEL SYSTEM

Stage 1

Delivery of units

Stage 2

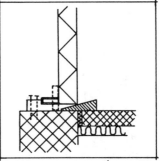

Setting out wall position

Stage 3

Prepare adhesive joints

Stage 4

Lift panels into position

Stage 5

Temporary props to panels

Stage 6

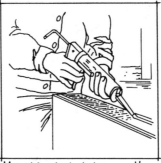

Mastic joint to wall intersection

Sequence of construction for internal panel walls

Figure 2.22

GASBETON LIGHTWEIGHT PANEL SYSTEM

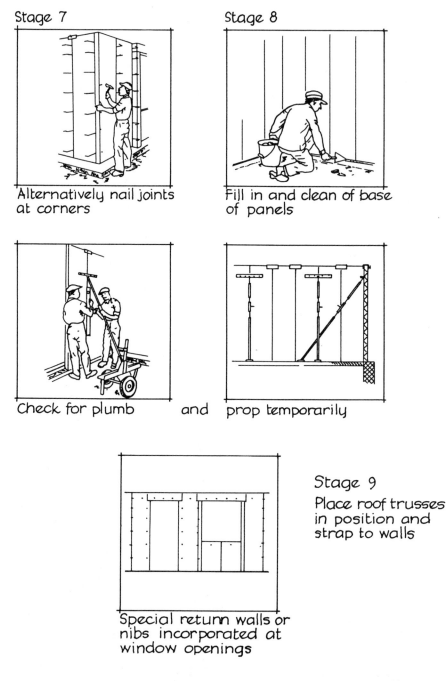

Stage 7

Alternatively nail joints at corners

Stage 8

Fill in and clean of base of panels

Check for plumb and prop temporarily

Stage 9
Place roof trusses in position and strap to walls

Special return walls or nibs incorporated at window openings

Sequence of construction for internal panel walls

Figure 2.23

GASBETON LIGHTWEIGHT PANEL SYSTEM

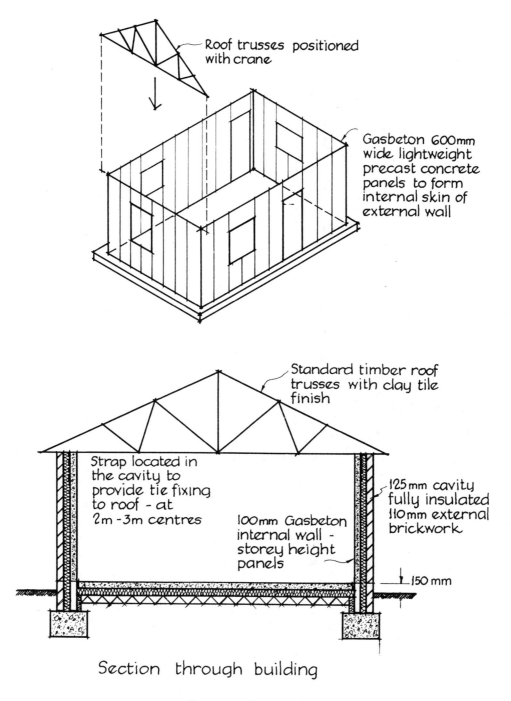

Roof trusses positioned with crane

Gasbeton 600mm wide lightweight precast concrete panels to form internal skin of external wall

Standard timber roof trusses with clay tile finish

Strap located in the cavity to provide tie fixing to roof - at 2m -3m centres

100mm Gasbeton internal wall - storey height panels

125mm cavity fully insulated 110mm external brickwork

150 mm

Section through building

Figure 2.24

GASBETON LIGHTWEIGHT PANEL SYSTEM

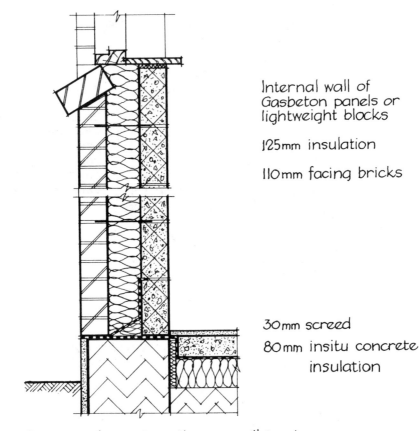

Internal wall of
Gasbeton panels or
lightweight blocks

125mm insulation

110mm facing bricks

30mm screed

80mm insitu concrete
insulation

Section through wall up to sill level

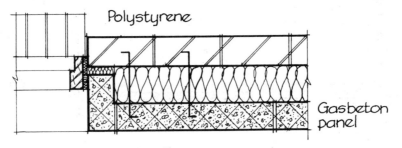

Polystyrene

Gasbeton
panel

Plan of external wall at door jamb

Figure 2.25

The main aim of a modular approach is to increase production in the building sector through increased productivity. In industrialised building, prefabricated components are used that do not require shaping at the building site.

A modular project, in the context of the Danish National Building Code, is a project in which the greatest possible number of prefabricated, standardised building components can be used.

2.14.2 Modular building applied to medium rise construction

Systems of construction for medium rise buildings may be categorised into a number of basic frame systems. These include:

    i)   Loadbearing wall frame systems
    ii)   Loadbearing wall and spine beam systems
   iii)   Loadbearing crosswall construction

1. Loadbearing wall frame construction

Figure 2.26 illustrates the principles of the wall frame system for the main building framework. The loads on the floors are carried by the walls supporting the slab edges on all four sides.

2. Loadbearing wall and spine beam system

Figure 2.27 illustrates the principles of the wall and spine beam form of frame construction. The loads from the single span floor units are carried on the external loadbearing wall and a central spine beam supported on columns.

3. Loadbearing crosswall construction

Figure 2.28 illustrates the principles of crosswall construction. The loads from the single span floor slab are carried down the crosswall the foundation level. Once again the flank walls or end panels are non-loadbearing and their weight is transmitted via supporting brackets located on the end of the crosswalls. The normal span of the crosswalls for medium rise buildings is approximately 4.8 metres. Systems have, however, been designed to accommodate crosswalls at centres of up to 8 metres.

The principles of the various building systems for medium rise structures has been explained using a simplistic approach. Further reference relating to the development of the Danish modular building systems should be made to the English translation of the Montagebyggeri.

LOADBEARING WALL FRAME SYSTEM

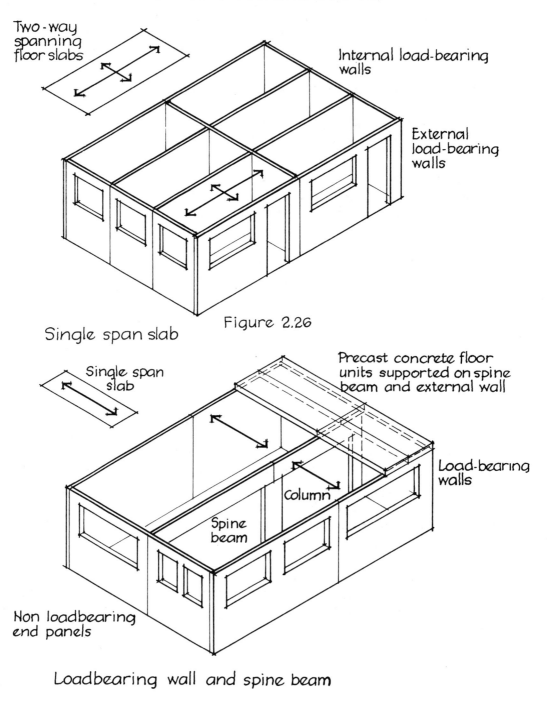

Two-way spanning floor slabs

Internal load-bearing walls

External load-bearing walls

Single span slab

Figure 2.26

Single span slab

Precast concrete floor units supported on spine beam and external wall

Load-bearing walls

Column

Spine beam

Non loadbearing end panels

Loadbearing wall and spine beam

Figure 2.27

LOADBEARING CROSSWALL SYSTEM

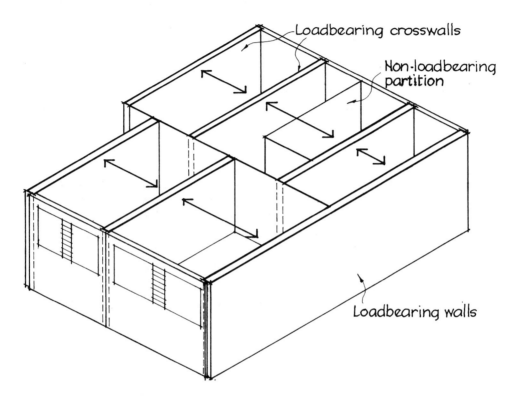

Loadbearing crosswalls

Non-loadbearing partition

Loadbearing walls

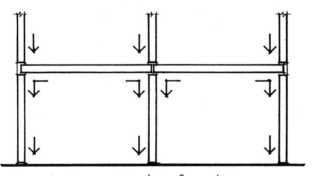

Loads transmitted to foundations via crosswalls

Figure 2.28

Figure 2.29 is a diagrammatic section through the external wall of the modular frame system. The 100 mm thick concrete wall panels form the internal walls of the building. A 125 mm layer of insulation slabs are fixed by patent ties to the wall face to provide cavity insulation. The outer face of the wall is built in facing bricks to provide a building elevation of traditional appearance. An exposed view of the arrangement of the precast concrete walls is shown, together with the temporary propping arrangement to the individual wall panels.

2.15 Case study of medium rise construction
The Frederiksgade project

Project information

The project involves the construction of 140 two to four person flats for a housing association. A layout plan of the project is shown in figure 2.30. Floor areas vary from 63 to 98 square metres per unit with rents in the order of 3000 Dkr to 4000 Dkr per month (£300-£400). The high rentable values reflects the high cost of living in Denmark.

Standards of construction are high with good quality finishes such as hardwood strip floors and good heating and thermal insulation standards. Figure 2.31 illustrates a ground floor plan layout of part of the complex, together with a sketch section through the building indicating the floor arrangements. The basement area provides facilities for parking.

2.15.1 Form of construction

The main building frame, forming the internal wall envelope, consists of a precast concrete loadbearing wall frame system. All wall panels are loadbearing and carry floor and wall loads down to the in situ concrete basement level.

2.15.2 Basement construction

Figure 2.32, detail A, indicates a section through the in situ concrete basement. The basement wall is constructed of 300 mm thick in situ concrete faced with dense concrete blocks above ground level. An 80 mm layer of polystyrene insulation is placed on the external face of the concrete wall below ground level. Above ground level the block wall is rendered externally.

LOADBEARING WALL SYSTEM

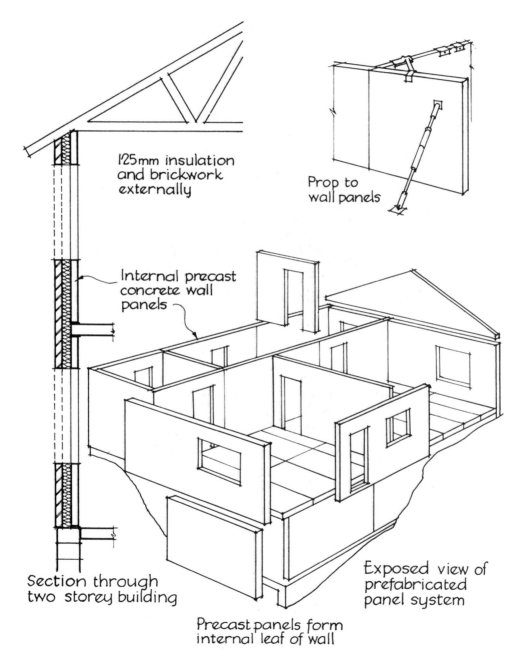

125mm insulation and brickwork externally

Prop to wall panels

Internal precast concrete wall panels

Section through two storey building

Exposed view of prefabricated panel system

Precast panels form internal leaf of wall

Figure 2.29

MEDIUM RISE CONSTRUCTION

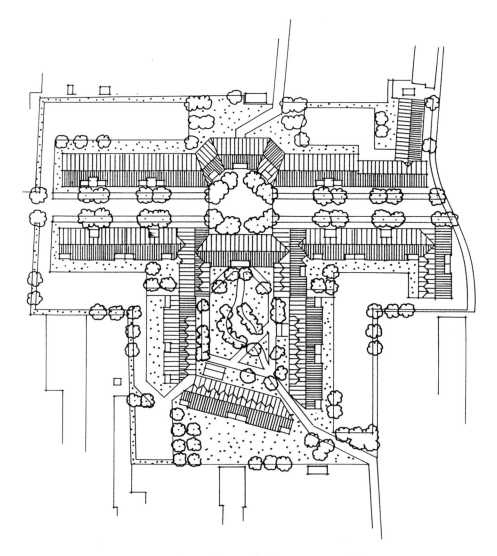

Layout Plan for Social Housing Scheme at
Frederiksgade - Horsens

Figure 2.30

LOADBEARING WALL FRAME SYSTEM

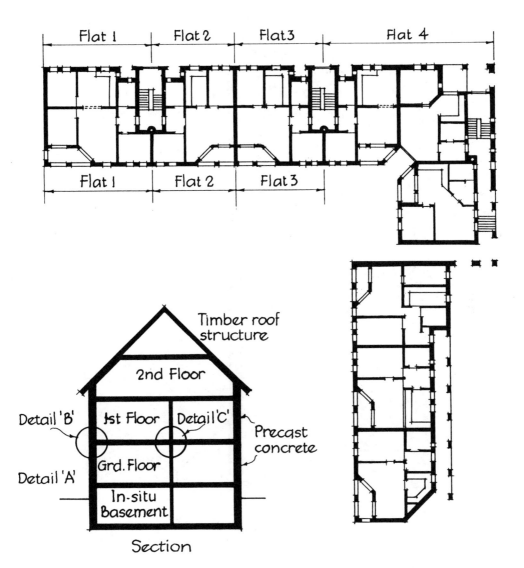

Layout Plan for Social Housing Flats
Project in Horsens

Figure 2.31

FOUNDATION CONSTRUCTION

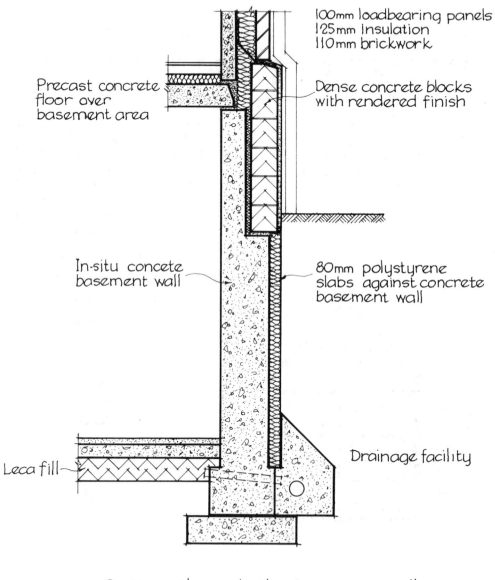

100mm loadbearing panels
125mm insulation
110mm brickwork

Precast concrete
floor over
basement area

Dense concrete blocks
with rendered finish

In-situ concete
basement wall

80mm polystyrene
slabs against concrete
basement wall

Leca fill

Drainage facility

Section through the basement wall

Detail 'A'

Figure 2.32

2.15.3 Frame and external wall construction

The loadbearing wall frame consists of 100 mm thick precast concrete units supporting 150 mm thick precast concrete widespan floor units. The precast wall panels form the internal wall enclosure of the building and the loadbearing walls between the flat units. Internally, the precast panels are pre-finished to receive a plaster skin coat prior to internal decoration. Building services are prelocated in the wall panels for electrical service points.

Externally, 125 mm insulation is applied to the external face of the precast panels and a 110 mm facing brick, this gives the appearance of a traditional brick building.

The precast concrete wallframe is first erected followed by the construction of the timber trussed roof. The exterior of the building is then scaffolded and the insulation and external brick facing are applied.

Figure 2.33 illustrates the construction detail at each floor level of the building showing the interrelationship between frame, floor and wall construction.

2.15.4 Jointing between wall frame units

Details of the joints between the precast wall and floor units are illustrated in detail B and C of the figure 2.34. Continuity reinforcement is positioned prior to the in situ concreting of the joint between floor and wall panels. Jointing principles are similar to those utilised in the British wallframe systems of the 1960s and 1970s buildings.

Figure 2.35 illustrates the forming of the in situ concrete vertical joint at the rear of adjacent wall panels. Here again, continuity reinforcement is positioned prior to concreting operations.

The Danish building regulations require a high degree of thermal insulation which results in a reduction in cold bridging problems. The flats are well insulated and adequately heated, resulting in a good degree of thermal comfort for the occupants of the building.

EXTERNAL WALL CONSTRUCTION

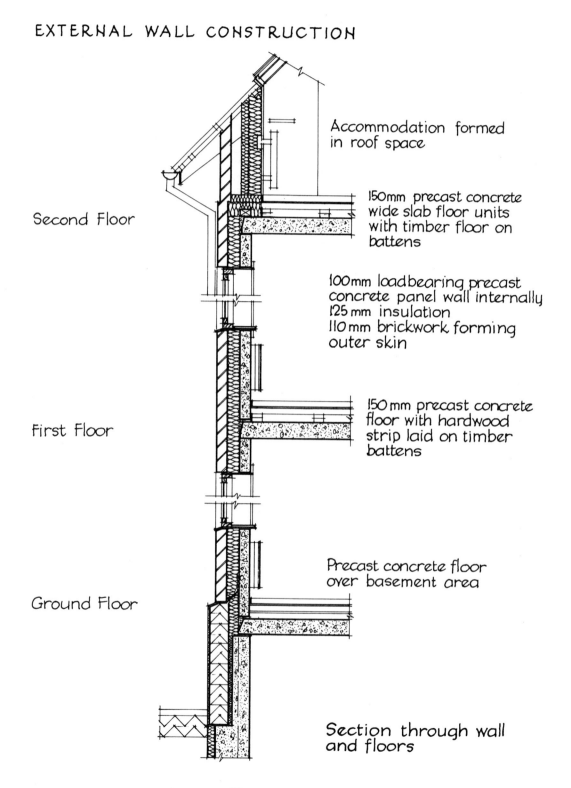

Accommodation formed in roof space

150mm precast concrete wide slab floor units with timber floor on battens

Second Floor

100mm loadbearing precast concrete panel wall internally
125mm insulation
110mm brickwork forming outer skin

150mm precast concrete floor with hardwood strip laid on timber battens

First Floor

Precast concrete floor over basement area

Ground Floor

Section through wall and floors

Figure 2.33

LOADBEARING FRAME CONSTRUCTION

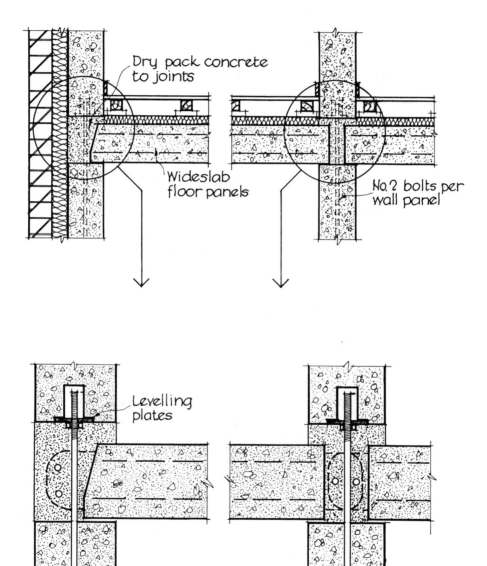

Dry pack concrete to joints

Wideslab floor panels

No. 2 bolts per wall panel

Levelling plates

Detail 'B'
External wall - inner leaf and floor joint

Detail 'C'
Internal wall and floor joint

Figure 2.34

LOADBEARING FRAME CONSTRUCTION

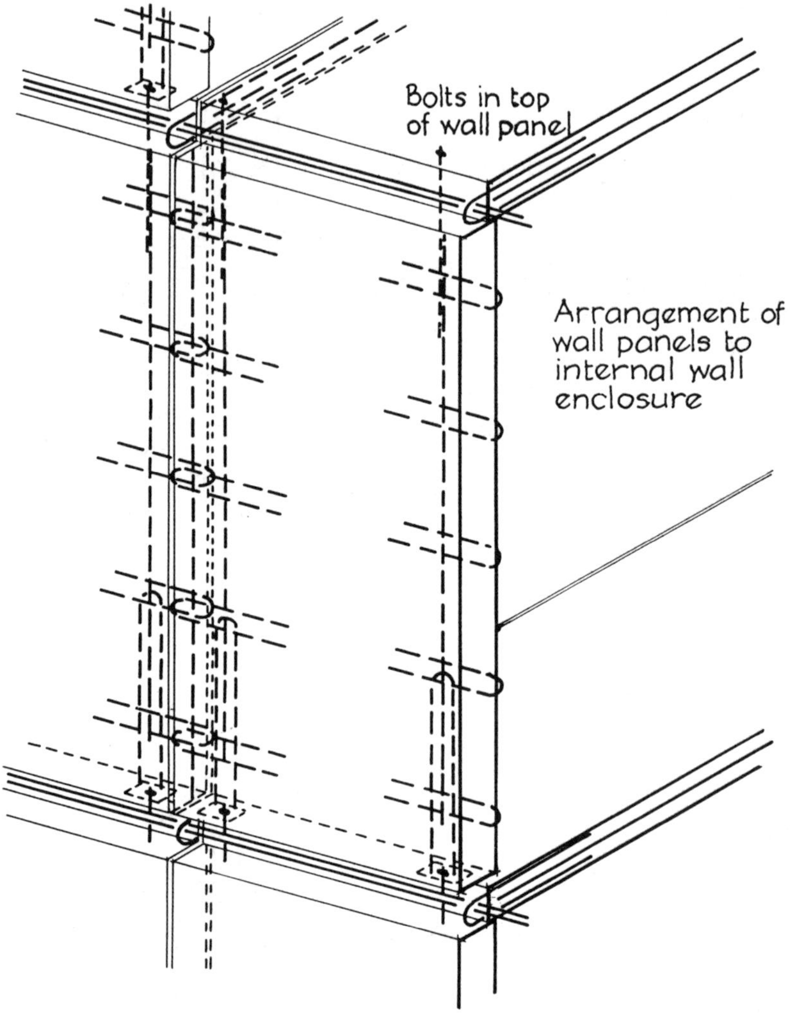

Bolts in top
of wall panel

Arrangement of
wall panels to
internal wall
enclosure

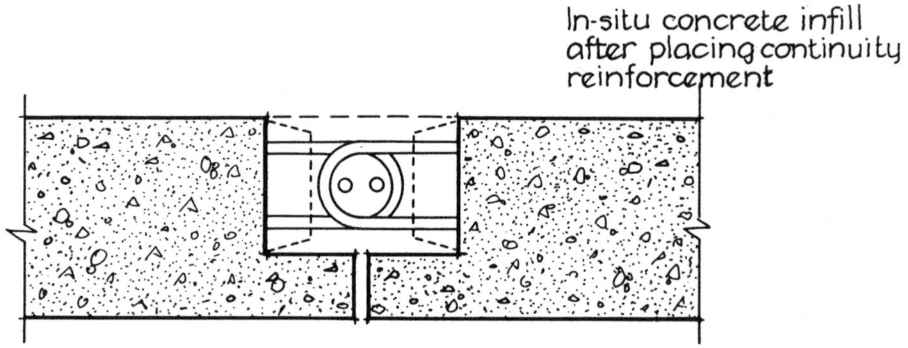

In-situ concrete infill
after placing continuity
reinforcement

Detail of joint between wall panels

Figure 2.35

3 The Construction Industry in France

3.1 Key information

Capital – Paris
Area (sq.km) 543 965   Population 57.46m (1992)

3.2 Construction output (1990)

Data obtained from the Euroconstruct Conference Report - June 1991

	ECU (Billion)
New residential construction	19.08
Private non-residential construction (offices, industrial, commercial)	12.26
Public non-residential construction (schools, universities, hospitals)	3.37
New civil engineering works including renovation in civil engineering	20.47
Renovation and modernisation in residential property	18.06
Non-residential renovation	12.43
Total	85.67

Current prices – 1 ECU = 6.914 FF (1990 average).

Building prices – labour and materials

Key labour rates for labour and craftsmen engaged in the construction industry are as shown. A range of key material prices is also given in order that comparisons may be made between each country discussed in the book.

Labour rate	Basic rate (per hour)	All-in-rate (per hour)
Unskilled labour	£4.28 (36 FF)	£9.40 (79 FF)
Craft operatives	£6.42 (54 FF)	£13.45 (113 FF)

Material	Unit	FF	£
High yield steel	Tonne	5800	690
Structural steel	Tonne	6750	804
Ordinary cement	Tonne	752	89
Carcasing	Cubic metre	1900	226
Clay bricks	1000	2100	231
Concrete	Square metre	32	3.86
Apartment	Square Metre		
	Range Low	4000	476
	High	7500	893
Factory units	Square Metre		
	Range Low	3000	357
	High	5000	595
Value Added Tax	General level 18.6%		
	Building rate 18.6%		

Data obtained from *Building* 22 January 1993, Procurement – European Costings

Total employees engaged in building	1 250 000 (1987)
Total employees engaged in civil engineering	260 000 (1987)

3.3 Review of the Construction Industry

Construction output in France in 1990 totalled around 86 billion ECU. This results in a building market of some 76% of the total. The pie chart in figure 3.1 indicates the division of work in both building, civil engineering, renovation and modernisation sectors. A detailed analysis of the work in each area is also shown. The number of contractors and the number of employees in relation to the size of the company is indicated.

DIVISION OF CONSTRUCTION OUTPUT 1990

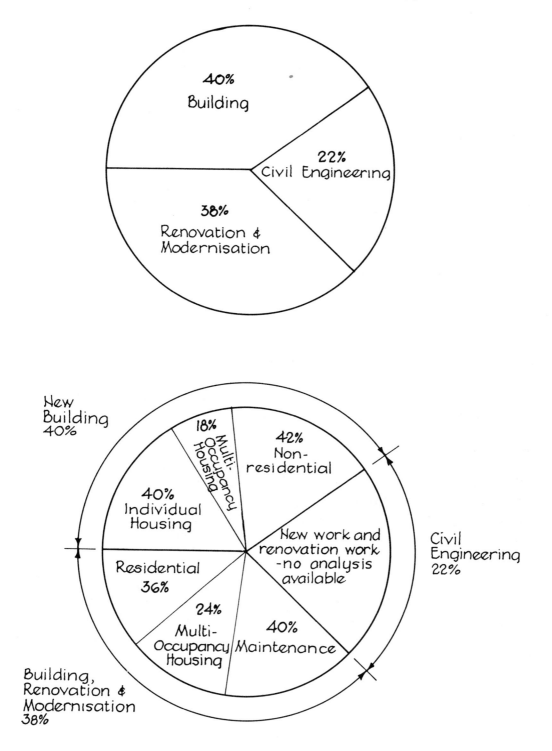

Figure 3.1

Number of employees	Contracting firms	
	260 000	
11 - 50	15 400	
51 - 200	1 400	Building firms
200 plus	185	
Major groups	8	

Number of employees		
	2 500	
11 - 50	2 235	
51 - 200	445	Civil Engineering
200 plus	105	
Major groups	22	

Major contracting organisations in France include:

Bouygues	GTM Entrepose
Campenon Bernard	SAE – Société Auxiliaire d'Entreprise
Dumez	SGE Group
Fougerolle	SOBEA and Spie Batignolles

During the past five years there have been a number of mergers in the construction industry resulting in the emergence of four major organisations:

	Annual Turnover 1987
Bouygues	£5 billion
GMT Entrepose and Dumez	£3 billion
SOGEA (merger of SGE and SOBEA)	£2.8 billion
Spie Batignolles	£1.89 billion

In 1992 Bouygues had the largest turnover of any building company in Europe. The French contracting organisations tend to undertake the majority of their work in contracting, with few companies engaging in a mixture of contracting and speculative development work. The separate trades system (*lot séparé*) is largely responsible for the proliferation of very small craft firms.

3.4 Extent of regionalisation

France is divided into twenty-two regions each with an elected council. Within the regions there are 36 500 communes, each with an elected council and mayor. The communes are directly responsible for matters relating to town planning, building and environmental issues.

A two-tier planning system is in operation in order to oversee the 30 year development plan for urban regions (*Schéma Directeur*) and a system of local plans (*Plan d'Occupation des Sols*) to service the communes.

3.5 The housebuilding industry

Over fifty per cent of the dwellings in France are owner occupied, thirty two percent are privately rented and the balance is made up of subsidised housing.

A comparison of the number of housing starts for the markets in France and the United Kingdom is as follows:

Year	France(000)	UK(000)
1980	420	162
1981	400	160
1982	343	202
1983	334	232
1984	295	207
1985	296	207
1986	296	219
1987	310	233
1988	291	214

Source – DOE Housing and construction statistics, Euroconstruct (SEG.No.138. 1987)

Speculative house building and the construction of residential flat development may be undertaken by clients or promoters. They are responsible for developing a workable scheme, seeking professional advice and arranging for the undertaking of the building works.

The separate trades contract arrangement will normally be used for the project, with the client's representative engaging a project co-ordinator to organise the subcontractors.

3.6 Relationships within the construction industry

The role of the participants in the construction industry involve:

The client – *Maître de l'ouvrage*
The client's representative – *Maître d'œuvre*
The architect – *Concepteur*
The BET – *Bureaux d'études techniques*
The project co-ordinator – *Pilote or Bureau du pilotage et d'ordonnancement*
The contractor – *L'entreprise général*
The technical control – *Bureau de controle*

The relationship between the participants is illustrated in figure 3.2 for a speculative project. Broad definitions of the roles involved in the construction process may be summarised as follows:

The client *(Maître de l'ouvrage)*
In both public and private projects the client is responsible for the complete building process. This involves land purchase, raising capital, establishing the brief and appointing the *maître d'œuvre*, architect and the *bureau d'etudes*.

The client's representative *(Maître d'œuvre)*
The maître d'œuvre may be either from an architectural or engineering discipline. In principle he is the leader of the building team and is responsible to the client for the concept, design and execution of the works. He controls the contracting procedures and deals with the financial accounting side of the project.

The architect *(Concepteur)*
The architect on a smaller project may have total responsibility for establishing the brief right through to the supervision of works, checking and approving certificates for payment and co-ordinating the work of the separate contractors.

On larger projects the architect may simply be responsible for the conceptual design, which is then developed by the *bureau d'études techniques* into working drawings.

The BET *(Bureau d'Études Techniques)*
The engaging of a bureau (or engineering consultancy group) is one of the main features of the French building industry. The BET is exclusively an engineering body involving all engineering disciplines; its members work in conjunction with the architect and develop his designs into working drawings for the contract.

RELATIONSHIP BETWEEN PARTIES
FOR A SPECULATIVE PROJECT

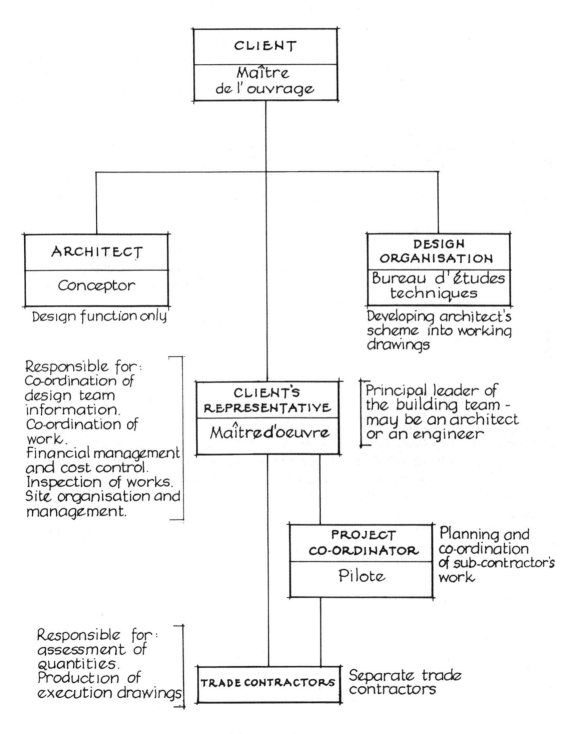

Figure 3.2

The project co-ordinator *(Pilote or Bureau de Pilotage et d'Ordonnancement)*
On both small and large contracts its often advantageous to engage a *pilote* to co-ordinate the work of the various trade contractors. Where a main contractor is controlling the work he may undertake the role of the *pilote* when co-ordinating the contractors under his control. In this case he is referred to as the *entrepreneur pilote*.

A growing necessity for separate engineering bodies to co-ordinate the work of a number of contractors on site has led to the establishment of a *Bureau de Pilotage et d'Ordonnancement*. The *pilotage* function involves the programming of each trade contractor in order to provide a production control service for the client.

The contractor *(L'entreprise général)*
The main contractor *(gros-œuvre)* on a major project is responsible for the co-ordination of the sub-contractors under his control. As indicated he may also act as *entrepreneur pilote* for the project. The French contractor very often has to produce his own working drawings which may be prepared by the *BET*, in house or by an independent consultant.

The technical control bureau *(Bureau de Contrôle)*
The bureau acts on behalf of an insurance company and is generally reimbursed by the contractor. The insurance companies will give no guarantee without the approval of the *Bureau de Contrôle* on the design and technical quality of the works. Working drawings and other technical documents must be approved by the BEC before work on site is commenced. Regular inspections of the work are carried out by the bureau during construction.

3.7 Role of the architect

Architects normally take a five-year course at any of the twenty-two courses of architecture at *Unités Pédagogiques d'Architecture* (UPA's), or at separate schools in Paris or Strasbourg. Any individual or organisation wishing to practice architecture must be registered with the Society of Architects (*l'Ordre des Architectes*). The applicant must have obtained an appropriate diploma and qualifications recognised by the Ministry of Culture.

The majority of architects in France undertake the preparation of sketch design schemes at the project feasibility stage. They do not normally produce working drawings as the client often prefers to use the services of the *Bureaux d'Études Techniques* (BET).

The law requires that there must be an architect engaged on a public sector building. In the case of private projects, the architect is required to sign and stamp the application for permission to construct (*permis de construire*).

This applies to work on buildings exceeding 170 square metres of floor area. There is no obligation on the client to employ the same architect, or indeed any architect, for work on the project once the permission has been obtained.

The majority of architects are engaged in private architectural practices, the average being two to three architects per practice. The architect who undertakes the design will often, in the public sector or private sector, act as the client for the construction work. He may also be responsible for ensuring that work on site proceeds smoothly.

Architects are prohibited from working for BETs or other commercial operations such as developers, contractors or estate agents.

The French architect's education is influenced strongly by the *beaux arts* tradition and concentrates on developing a liberal approach to design. The architect is not highly regarded by other members of the construction industry, nor is the public image of the profession very high. The profession is devoting considerable efforts to correct some of the difficulties in architectural education, and is slowly adopting a more practical approach.

3.8 Role of the engineer

Engineers first undertake a two-year preparatory course at an *École* prior to spending a further three years at a school of engineering. On completion of the course of study the student is awarded an engineer's diploma (*ingénieur diplôme*).

As an alternative, students may take a five-year course at a university. Facilities are also available for technician engineers to proceed to professional level by pursuing a distance learning course of study. The student is also required to prepare a thesis on an engineering matter prior to being granted an engineer's diploma.

The engineer is the dominant profession in France. Engineers are involved in design, consultancy and in the BET (*bureau d'études techniques*). The engineer also carries out many of the functions of both the building surveyor and quantity surveyor.

The engineer is the principal designer for most infrastructure and public works, where the client is mainly in the public sector. Engineers are directly employed by client bodies or ministries. Most of the design work is undertaken by them and they normally act as the client's representative during the project.

The engineer will normally appoint a team to undertake the design and supervision of the construction stages. In practice, engineers specialise in the design or the construction process – although there are no formal subdivisions into civil engineers, structural engineers or services engineers. French engineers are well trained and generally of a high calibre. They often reach high positions in management in both the public and private sectors.

The title of *'ingénieur'* is not a protected title. The term engineer may apply to many personnel engaged in construction activities, i.e. design engineers, site engineers, sales engineers, etc.

Role of the bureau d'études techniques (BET) or design organisations

The majority of the design organisations are commercially oriented. The most common of these are the BETs. These design organisations may be owned by contractors or be integrated within client organisations in the public sector; alternatively, they may be owned by industrial companies. The design organisations are often responsible for interpreting the architect's designs into detailed and working drawings from which the project may be constructed.

The tendering system in France allows for alternative designs to be put forward by the contractors. Here again the contractor may engage a BET to prepare the working drawings from the scheme on which the tender was based.

As an alternative to using a BET, the design may be developed by engaging an independent consulting engineer (*ingénieur conseil*).

3.9 Role of the quantity surveyor

The *métreur* (measurer) and the *vérificateur* (verifier) come nearest to carrying out the function and services provided by the quantity surveyor in the United Kingdom. Their service is regarded as a technical service and is not considered to be on the same professional level as that of the architect or the engineer.

The *métreur* may be engaged by the architect or the engineer or he may work on behalf of the contractor.

The *vérificateur*, on the other hand, essentially represents the architect/engineer or client in the checking of work done by the contractor at the various payment stages of the work.

The *métreur* is experienced in the measurement of work during the design process and may undertake the preparation of the cost estimates at the design stage (budget estimates). His services may be extended to cover the analysis of the bids submitted by the various contractors.

Where the *métreur* is engaged by the contractor he may assist in the preparation of the estimates by providing a measurement service, as well as participating in the estimating function. During the construction stage he may prepare monthly valuations, maintain site records and be responsible for the preparation of the final account, i.e. acting in a similar role to the contractor's surveyor in the United Kingdom.

The role of the *métreur* and the *vérificateur* in relation to the contractual arrangements is shown in figure 3.3.

The majority (87%) of the measurers and verifiers work in private practice; there are approximately 1500 practices of construction economists in France. The balance mainly work for contractor organisations (which include BETs) and the public sector.

The organisation that represents the principal in private practice is UNTEC – *Union Nationale des Techniciens Économistes de la Construction*.

In addition to the measurer who undertakes the role of the quantity surveyor, there is support available at a lower technician level (personnel holding the *Brevet de Technicien* qualification).

Educational requirements leading to the qualification of a measurer are:

***Brevet de Technicien* (BT)** – this is the equivalent to the baccalaureate standard; the student is awarded a technician certificate from one of the many technical high school institutions (*Écoles de l'Éducation Nationale*).

***Brevet de Technicien Supérieur* (BTS)** – a higher technician certificate. This involves an additional two years of study beyond the BT level and is undertaken at any one of ten advanced technical institutions (*Écoles de l'Éducation Nationale*).

3.10 Contractual arrangements and building procurement

The various methods of procuring construction work by the client may be summarised as:

(i) Separate trade contracts – *Lots séparés*
(ii) Main contract arrangement
(iii) Group contractor arrangements – *Groupement des Entreprises Solidaires* and *Groupement Conjoint.*

3.10.1 Separate trade contracts – Lots séparés

This type of contractual arrangement involves the client letting separate contracts with each trade sub-contractor or group of sub-contractors.

Figure 3.4 indicates the situation where the project is under the control of the client's representative (*maître d'ouvrage*) who may be an engineer or architect. The scheme concept and the outline design is undertaken by an architect and the working drawings are prepared by the *Bureau d'Études Techniques* (BET). The client's representative is responsible for the technical, financial and quality control of the project.

CONSTRUCTION INDUSTRY RELATIONSHIPS

Function \ Participant	ARCHITECT	BUREAUX D'ÉTUDES	CONSULTING ENGINEER	PUBLIC SECTOR DESIGN OFFICE	METREUR/VÉRIFICATEUR	PILOTE	CONTRACTOR
CLIENT'S REPRESENTATIVE	F	O	O	F			
PILOTE	O	O			O	F	F
CONCEPTUAL DESIGN	F	O		O			
DETAIL DESIGN / DRAWINGS	F	F		O			O
ENGINEERING DESIGN		F	F	F			O
WORKING DRAWINGS			O				F
CONTRACT DOCUMENTATION	F	F	O	O	F		
SITE SUPERVISION	F	F	O	F			
COST CONTROL	O	O		F	F		

F - Frequently

O - Occasionally

Relationship between Function and Participant during the construction process

Figure 3.3

CONTRACTUAL RELATIONSHIP WITH
CLIENT'S REPRESENTATIVE (MAÎTRE D'OEUVRE)

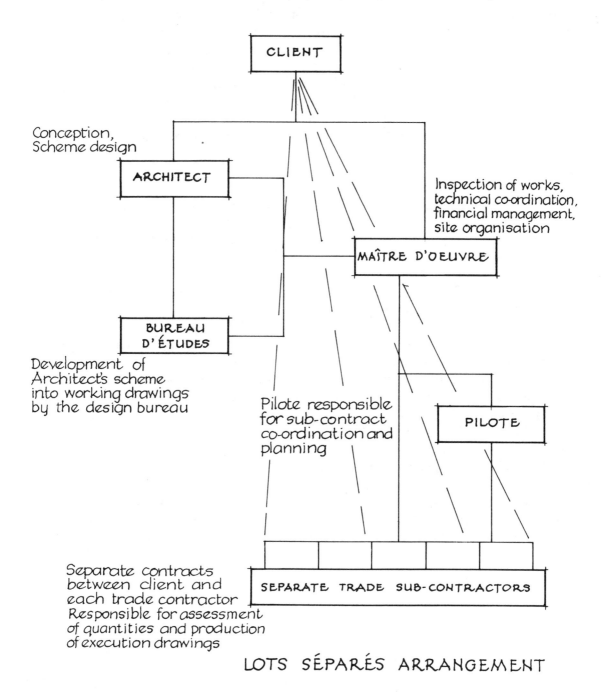

LOTS SÉPARÉS ARRANGEMENT

Figure 3.4

A *pilote* is engaged to co-ordinate the organisation and planning of the separate trade sub-contractors. The client is responsible for the payment of fees to the design team and pilote.

Figure 3.5 indicates a contractual relationship where the architect undertakes the role of contract manager, and consultants have been engaged to develop the structural design, services and interior design. A trade contractor specialising in reinforced concrete framed construction has been employed for the structural work. The trades contractor may sub-let to other sub-contractors on a supply and fix basis. The sub-contractor must be declared to the client and may be contracted and paid direct by the client from the outset.

Sub-contract work packages can be progressively awarded during the design stage of the project. On completion of the building frame a finishing trades contractor may be brought in to complete the building interior.

The main form of standard contract is to the *Code des Marches Publiques* on which private sector contracts are based. The principal components of the contract are:

(i) The *Acte d'Engagement* (Articles of Agreement)
(ii) *Cahier des Clauses d'Administration Générales* (General contract administration clauses)
(iii) *Cahier des Clauses Techniques Générales* (General technical clauses relating to standards and codes of practice)

Together, the above documents are referred to as the **Cahier des Charges** and are equivalent to UK contract preliminaries and specification as in the JCT contract (without quantities).

The measurement of quantities lies entirely with the trade sub-contractor who will be responsible for the production of his own working drawings.

Strict project control is required by the client's representative and the *pilote*. Project planning and co-ordination are key factors to the success of the *Lots Séparés* contract arrangement.

3.10.2 *Main contractor arrangement*

This method of contractual arrangement is used on major complex projects where the client prefers to deal with a single party. The main contractor generally undertakes up to 25% of the work and is responsible for co-ordinating the work of the sub-contract trades.

CONTRACT RELATIONSHIP WITH
ARCHITECT CONTRACT MANAGER

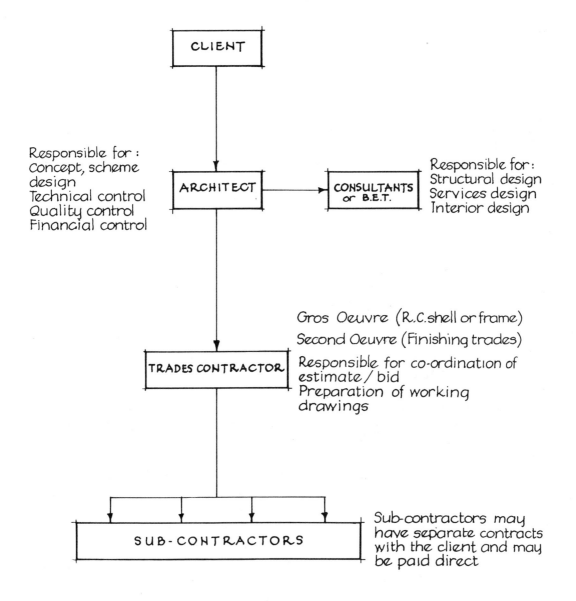

CLIENT

Responsible for :
Concept, scheme
design
Technical control
Quality control
Financial control

ARCHITECT

CONSULTANTS
or B.E.T.

Responsible for:
Structural design
Services design
Interior design

Gros Oeuvre (R.C. shell or frame)

Second Oeuvre (Finishing trades)

TRADES CONTRACTOR

Responsible for co-ordination of
estimate / bid
Preparation of working
drawings

SUB-CONTRACTORS

Sub-contractors may
have separate contracts
with the client and may
be paid direct

LOTS SÉPARÉS ARRANGEMENT

Figure 3.5

For small contracts, where it is unrealistic to appoint separate trade subcontracts as in the *lots séparés* system, the client may appoint the small works department of a large contracting organisation to undertake the role of the main contractor.

Figure 3.6 illustrates the contractual relationships between the parties involved.

3.10.3 Group sub-contractor arrangements – Groupement Conjoint and Groupement des Entreprises Solidaires

The client may ask for tenders on separate trades and some of the sub-contractors may decide to group their tenders together in the form of a group bid (*groupement conjoint*). In this arrangement the client may formally divide the contract up into a number of defined packages and obtain group quotations for the work. This system is used extensively throughout France and is one of the most common methods of procurement. Using the groupement conjoint arrangement a co-ordinator or *pilote* will usually be appointed to oversee the planning of the work.

Figure 3.7 indicates the relationship between the parties involved in the construction process. The above may also be referred to as a joint venture contract arrangement.

3.10.4 Tendering arrangements

The invitation to tender process is termed the *appel d'offres*. Tendering options are similar to those in the United Kingdom; open tendering, selective tendering and negotiated contracts are all used

The client will normally have decided, in advance of issuing tender invitations, upon the contracting system that he wishes to use (*lots séparés*, main contractor or *groupement conjoint arrangement*).

Tenders are usually based on the specification and scheme drawings which may be in the form of sketch plans. The tender documents are prepared by the architect or engineer in conjunction with a measurer (*métreur*).

Each contractor who tenders has to determine the method of construction to be used and this may involve consideration of which form of building frame would be most economically viable. Bids submitted may therefore vary widely, depending upon the contractor's assessment of the client's requirements.

Contractors preparing bids will call on the assistance of a measurer to assist with the preparation of the estimate. Advice will also be sought from the BET regarding the most economic design considerations and form of construction to be adopted. The quotation submitted will also have to include an amount for the contractor employing the BET to later develop the tender drawings into working drawings for construction purposes.

MAIN CONTRACTOR ARRANGEMENT

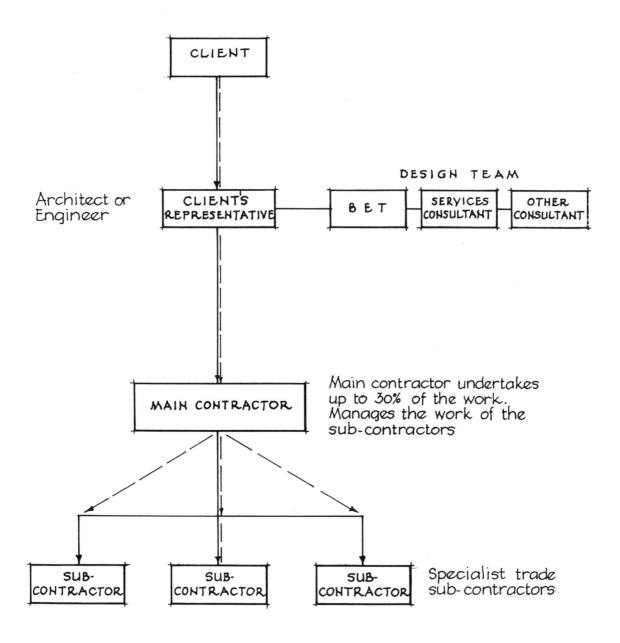

Figure 3.6

GROUP SUB-CONTRACTOR ARRANGEMENT –
GROUP CONJOINT

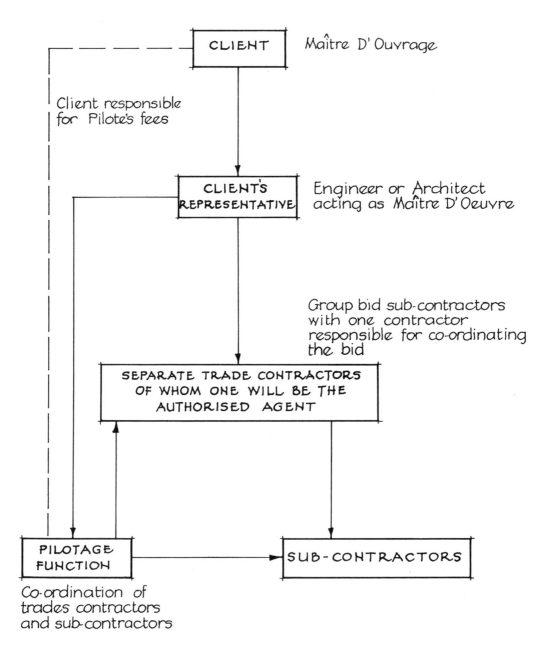

Figure 3.7

Open tendering may be used for major contracts which may stimulate competitive interest from contractors throughout the European Community. This may take the form of press advertisements in international journals inviting major contractors to apply for the project information. This process may be used to establish a shortlist for the submission of bids.

A £100 million contract for the construction of a national sports stadium in Manchester has recently resulted in four contractors being shortlisted from thirty enquiries. The shortlist included three United Kingdom consortia and one French consortium. The design teams preparing the bids for the various consortia included many international architects and consulting engineers of world repute.

Where selective tendering is preferable, the number of contractors invited to tender varies according to the size of the project. Four to six general contractors may be invited to bid for contracts between £1.5 to £6.5 million. For separate subcontractor bids, four or five will be invited to tender for the main trades and two or three for the lesser trades.

3.11 Planning and building control procedures

The control of development in France is based on obtaining a permit to construct. This applies to virtually all construction works and must be submitted by an architect.

Development control is governed by the following codes:

> *Code d'Urbanisme*
> *Code de l'Environnement*
> *Code de la Construction* (the building regulations)

The application for permission to construct (*permis de construire*) covers both the planning permission and the building regulations. This is deposited with the mayor of the *commune* in which the application is made. The submission is processed in conformity with the *Code d'Urbanisme* by the state planning representative.

The technical bureau is engaged by the client to check the drawings and the impact of the works on the site. The employment of the technical bureau (*bureau de contrôle* or *contrôleurs techniques*) is a compulsory requirement for insurance purposes. The bureaus approved by the state for undertaking this role are the Bureau Vertic'as, SOCTEC and CEP. In principle, the technical bureaus act in the role of building control.

The building permit is a means of ensuring that the proposed building application complies with the rules of the *Code d'Urbanisme* and is required to satisfy regional and local planning policies. If the commune has approved the local plan (*Plan d'Occupation des Sols*), then the mayor takes the decision to grant or refuse planning permission and sign the permit.

Technical control procedures

Technical control of construction work is carried out by the municipality and comes into effect once the building permit has been issued.

The building designer is responsible for ensuring that the design and standards comply with all applicable regulations and construction requirements.

During the execution of the work inspection is carried out on site by a technical inspector employed by the municipal authority. Inspection is undertaken at two stages of the construction. The first takes place on excavation of the foundations. The second, on the completion of the foundations. On completion of the work an occupation licence is issued.

3.12 Low rise housing construction

Information collection

The case study material outlined in the text relates to a number of housing projects in the Caen and Nantes regions of France.

Data relating to the construction techniques has been obtained from current trade literature and from visits to residential housing and flat projects.

The construction techniques dealt with may not be typical of the building methods utilised in other parts of the country.

3.12.1 Form of construction

Low rise construction techniques basically fall into two categories:

1.   Dwellings constructed of 200 mm thick dense concrete block to form the external walls of the building. At first floor level the walls support prestressed concrete beam and block floors. It is common practice to incorporate an in situ concrete spine beam to carry the floor at first floor level. This may be supported on columns or on strengthened blockwork.

The external block walls are lined internally with polystyrene insulation slabs which incorporate a plasterboard finish. Externally the block walls are rendered and painted. Traditional cavity wall construction, as utilised in the United Kingdom, is rarely used.

2. Dwellings constructed of in situ concrete walls and floors. In situ concrete walls are utilised to form the external envelope and party walls. Extensive use is made of site precasting techniques for balcony decks and plank floors.

    The concrete walls are lined internally with polystyrene insulated panels which incorporate a plasterboard finish for direct painting. Externally the in situ concrete walls are painted.

In northern France roof construction is based on trussed rafters and finished in concrete tiles or neuralite black slates. Extensive use is made of dormers and varying roof slopes. In southern France, Roman style pantiles are used extensively.

The garage to a house may be attached or alternatively constructed under part of the house as part of a basement area. This is dependent upon the house style and the availability of land around the property and site ground levels.

A variety of housing designs typical of those found on speculative developments in the western region of France are illustrated in figures 3.8.

Case studies are presented on a number of low rise housing projects in order to illustrate clearly the construction techniques adopted.

Reference information on French building techniques

Data on building methods for low rise buildings has also been obtained from two excellent books written by H. Renaud and published by Les Editions Foucher.

Constructeur Bâtiment Technologie – 1 and 2, (1985).

These references provide a practical insight into French building techniques for low rise construction. A further reference by H. Renaud and F.Laterie deals with the construction of multi-storey framed buildings,

Technologie du Bâtiment Gros-œuvre. (1978).

3.13 Case study in low rise housing

3.13.1 Development layout

Figure 3.9 illustrates the site location plan for the development together with the proximity of highways and buildings adjacent to the project.

LOW RISE HOUSING DESIGN

Detached

Three bedrooms with carport/ garage

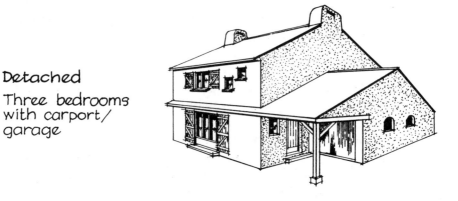

Bungalow Type

Detached

Four bedrooms

Figure 3.8

A detailed location plan of the plot is shown in figure 3.10 together with the dimensions of the adjacent plot. The overall plot dimensions are indicated, together with dimensions from the external walls to the site boundaries.

3.13.2 House plans and elevations

Figures 3.11 to 3.12 illustrate the front elevation, cross section and ground floor plan of a two-storey detached residence.

3.13.3 Foundations element

Foundations may be of the strip or raft type. Details of a concrete strip foundation supporting a solid ground floor are shown in figure 3.13. It is normal practice to provide thermal insulation to the perimeter of the ground floor slab extending a minimum of one metre under the floor. An alternative raft foundation detail is also shown.

It is common practice to provide a shallow land drain facility around the perimeter of the foundation. This is in order to prevent any ground water gaining contact with the wall foundation and create rising damp problems in the external wall. Ground floors may be constructed of in situ concrete laid directly on a compacted foundation. Suspended reinforced slabs may be incorporated using in situ or precast concrete construction.

The commencement of the external blockwork construction is shown in figure 3.14 and special corner blocks incorporating a 150 mm square pocket are built in to provide additional wall stability. Reinforcement is positioned at foundation level and the void filled with in situ concrete to form a column. Figure 3.15 indicates the details of a suspended precast concrete floor at the junction with the external wall.

3.13.4 Foundation element incorporating a basement area

It is common practice on residential housing developments to construct basement garage areas. This is dependent upon the levels on site and the space available on the plot for the ramp access into the garage. Habitable rooms located in the basement area are not however an essential part of the housing construction, as they are in Germany.

Figure 3.16 illustrates a dwelling with a part basement area. Again, drainage facilities are incorporated to reduce the build-up of groundwater pressure on the basement walls.

Methods of waterproofing the basement area are shown in figures 3.17 to 3.18. The basement walls may be constructed of in situ concrete incorporating an asphaltic membrane. Alternatively, block walls may be specified which may be SIKA rendered externally as illustrated in figure 3.18.

LOW RISE HOUSING DESIGN

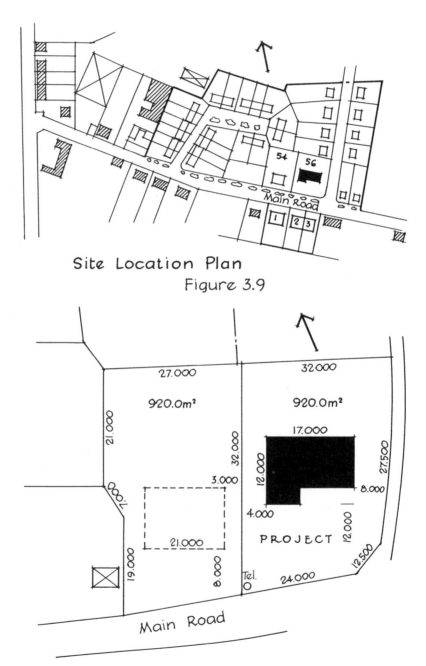

Site Location Plan

Figure 3.9

Detailed Location Plan

Figure 3.10

LOW RISE HOUSING DESIGN

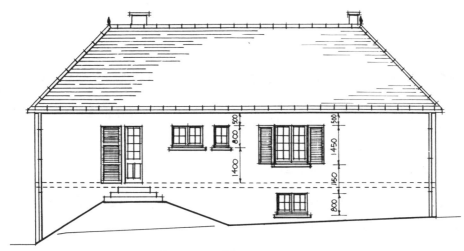

Front Elevation

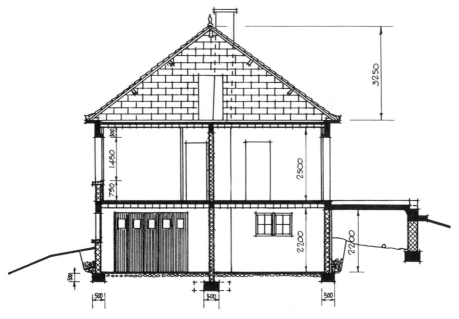

Cross Section

Figure 3.11

LOW RISE HOUSING DESIGN

Front

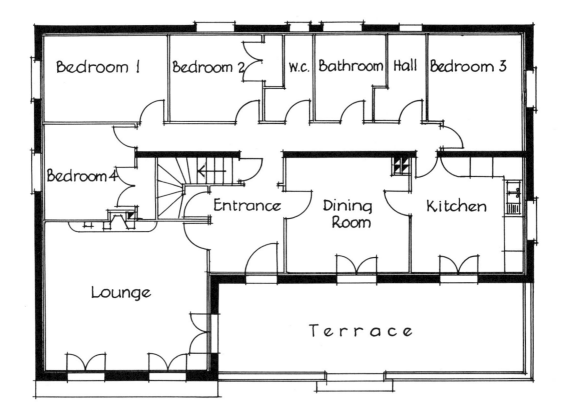

Rear

Ground Floor Plan

Scale 1:100

Figure 3.12

FOUNDATION CONSTRUCTION

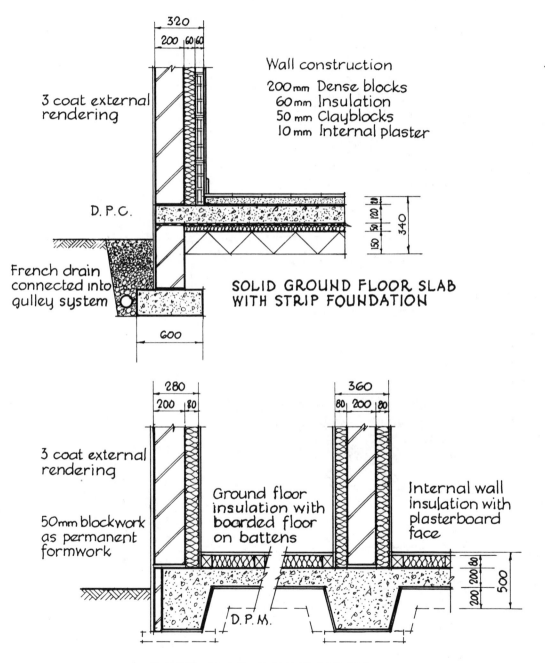

320

200 | 60 | 60

3 coat external rendering

Wall construction

200mm Dense blocks
60mm Insulation
50mm Clayblocks
10mm Internal plaster

D.P.C.

French drain connected into gulley system

SOLID GROUND FLOOR SLAB WITH STRIP FOUNDATION

600

280

200 | 80

3 coat external rendering

50mm blockwork as permanent formwork

Ground floor insulation with boarded floor on battens

360

80 | 200 | 80

Internal wall insulation with plasterboard face

D.P.M.

RAFT SLAB FOUNDATION

Figure 3.13

FOUNDATION CONSTRUCTION

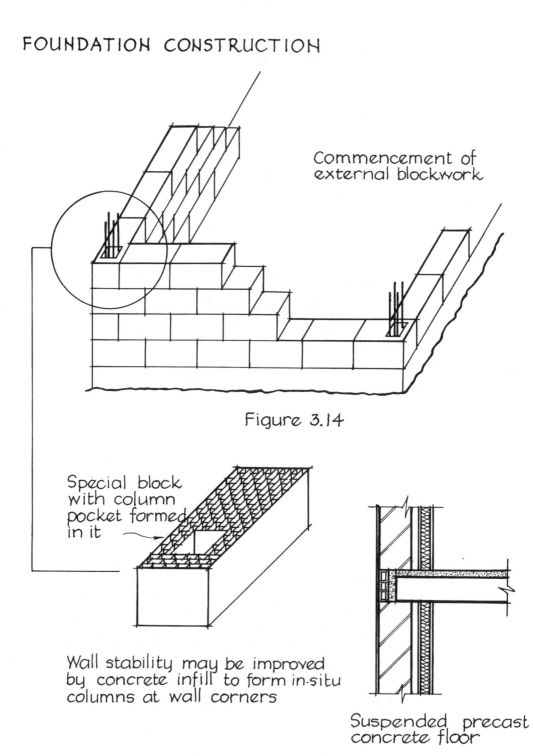

Commencement of external blockwork

Figure 3.14

Special block with column pocket formed in it

Wall stability may be improved by concrete infill to form in-situ columns at wall corners

Suspended precast concrete floor

Figure 3.15

FOUNDATION CONSTRUCTION - BASEMENTS

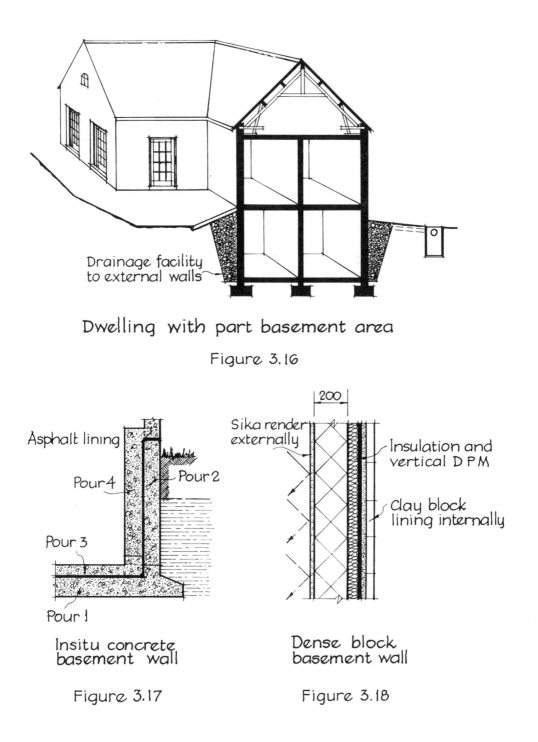

Drainage facility
to external walls

Dwelling with part basement area

Figure 3.16

Asphalt lining

Pour 4

Pour 2

Pour 3

Pour 1

Insitu concrete
basement wall

Figure 3.17

200

Sika render
externally

Insulation and
vertical DPM

Clay block
lining internally

Dense block
basement wall

Figure 3.18

Good practice requirements indicate the need for the provision of adequate drainage to the basement area. Various ways of meeting these provisions are illustrated in figure 3.19.

3.13.5 External wall element

External wall construction consists of 200 mm thick dense concrete blocks. The external walls support the loading from the first floor. The block walls may be stiffened by incorporating in situ concrete infill columns at the wall junctions and corners; this is facilitated by using a special concrete block which incorporates provision for the in situ column. Figure 3.20 illustrates the incorporation of an insitu concrete column and spine beam which supports the precast beam and block first floor it also provides an open area to the ground floor lounge. In situ concrete lintels are generally installed over door and window openings compared with precast reinforced concrete or steel lintels used in the UK.

3.13.6 Internal lining to the external walls

Cavity wall construction is rarely utilised in France. The practice adopted is to provide an insulated lining to the external wall. This involves lining the wall internally using polystyrene insulated slabs incorporating a vapour barrier and plasterboard face. The procedure for fixing the internal lining is illustrated in figure 3.21.

As an alternative, mineral wool slabs may be used in conjunction with 50 mm wide cellular blocks which are plastered on completion.

3.13.7 Thermal insulation requirements

The thermal insulation requirements for domestic dwellings are illustrated in figure 3.22. Insulation requirements are indicated for an adjoining building situation and for a unit containing a basement area. The insulation requirements must satisfy the French codes of practice – AF NOR DTU P50 – 702 and NFX 02-006. The methods of providing thermal insulation for external walls are illustrated in figures 3.13 and 3.21.

3.13.8 Floor construction

It is general practice to specify prestressed beam floors incorporating a variety of infill blocks. The prestressed beams require propping at 1500 mm to 2000 mm centres prior to placing the in situ concrete structural slab.

BASEMENT WALL CONSTRUCTION AND DRAINAGE FACILTY PROVISIONS

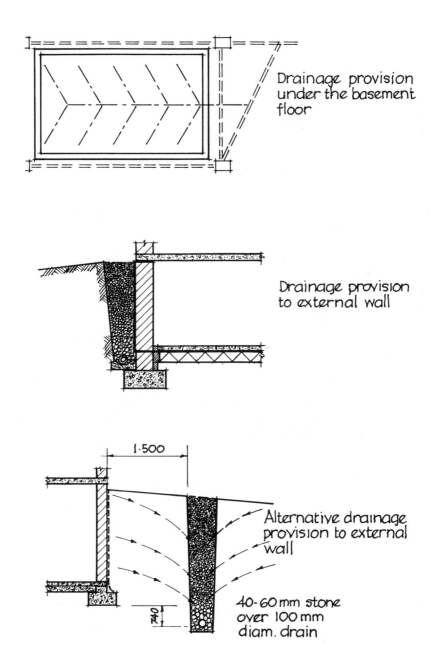

Drainage provision under the basement floor

Drainage provision to external wall

1·500

Alternative drainage provision to external wall

740

40-60 mm stone over 100 mm diam. drain

Figure 3.19

EXTERNAL WALL CONSTRUCTION

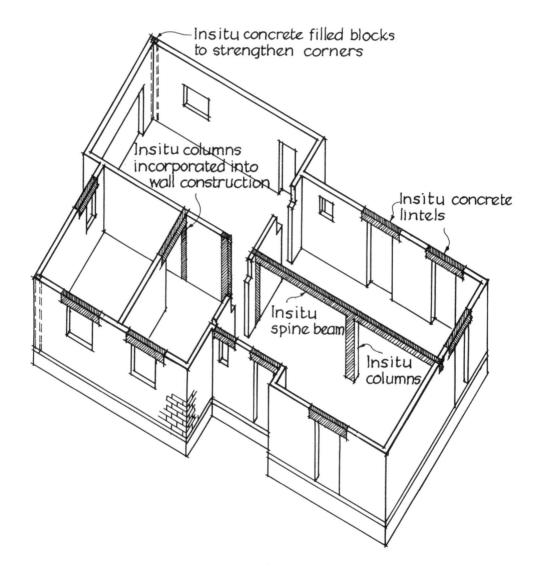

Wall construction incorporating insitu
concrete columns and spine beam

Figure 3.20

EXTERNAL WALL CONSTRUCTION

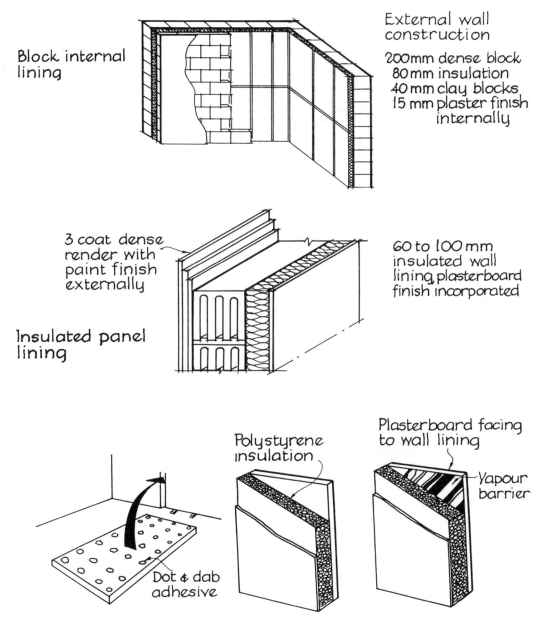

Block internal lining

External wall construction

200mm dense block
80mm insulation
40mm clay blocks
15mm plaster finish
internally

3 coat dense render with paint finish externally

Insulated panel lining

60 to 100mm insulated wall lining, plasterboard finish incorporated

Polystyrene insulation

Plasterboard facing to wall lining

Vapour barrier

Dot & dab adhesive

Internal lining to block walls

Figure 3.21

THERMAL INSULATION REQUIREMENTS
('U' VALUES)

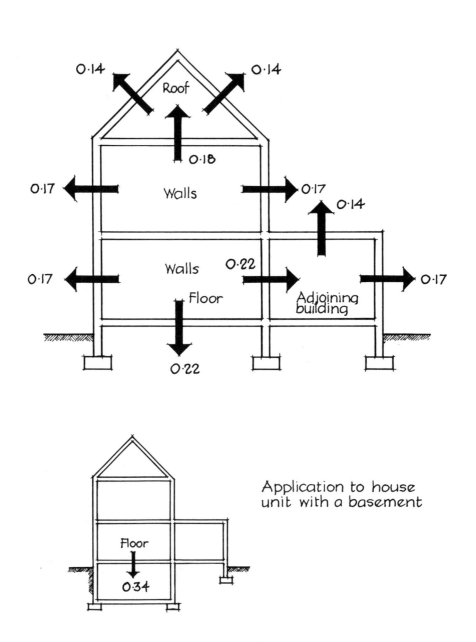

French Code   AF NOR DTU P50-702
NFX 02-006

Figure 3.22

A floor spanning on to a central spine beam is illustrated in figure 3.23 and a floor spanning on to the top of a 200 mm thick block wall is shown in figure 3.24.

In order to meet the insulation requirements it is necessary to provide some degree of insulation within the floor construction. Figure 3.25, details A to D, indicates alternative ways of achieving the insulation requirements.

3.13.9 Roof construction

Roof construction for low rise housing generally consists of timber rafters, purlins and ceiling joists similar to traditional construction methods in the United Kingdom. Patent timber roof trusses are also in common use.

Roof finishes consist of a wide range of concrete and clay tiles including the extensive use of neuralite black slates. Roof shapes vary from simple gabled and hipped roofs through to turreted roofs typical of the French *château* style. Extensive use is made of roof overhangs and dormers.

3.14 Medium rise construction

Form of construction

For medium rise flats constructed for social housing or residential accommodation various forms of construction may be used for the main building frame. Forms of construction include the following:

1. Buildings constructed of reinforced concrete frames. The frame may incorporate in situ downstand beams and floors. As an alternative, precast concrete floors may be incorporated.

2. Buildings constructed of dense concrete block loadbearing walls supporting in situ concrete floors. The 200 mm dense blocks act as the internal skin of the external wall. Thermal insulation is applied to the outer face of the block walls and facing bricks are laid to form the outer skin.

3. Crosswall construction incorporating insitu concrete walls and precast concrete floors. Extensive use is made of site precasting techniques for the plank floors as illustrated in the case study of Nantes University in 3.15.

Site precasting procedures are widely adopted on construction sites for floors, columns and beams; this is a feature rarely observed in other European countries.

SUSPENDED BEAM AND BLOCK FLOORS

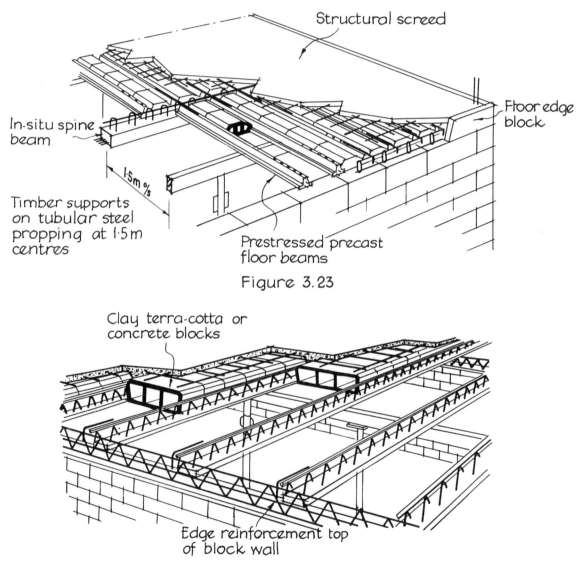

Structural screed

In·situ spine beam

Floor edge block

1·5m c/s

Timber supports on tubular steel propping at 1·5m centres

Prestressed precast floor beams

Figure 3.23

Clay terra·cotta or concrete blocks

Edge reinforcement top of block wall

Figure 3.24

SUSPENDED CONCRETE FLOORS

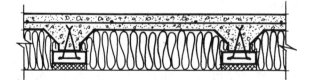

Polystyrene formers positioned between precast concrete beams. Structural screed placed over units.

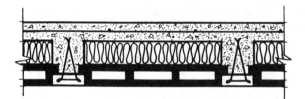

Clay terra-cotta blocks with polystyrene formers placed over them

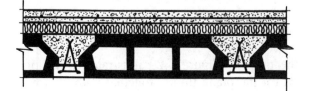

Beam and infill blocks with concrete infill. Insulation and structural screed placed over them

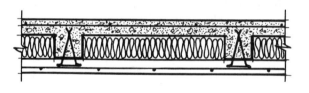

Polystyrene formers placed on plank floor units. Concrete infill screed placed over floor prior to laying finishes

Figure 3.25

3.15 Case study in medium rise construction
Student accommodation at Nantes University

Introduction

The project consists of the construction of two four-storey blocks, each containing eighty flat units, to provide student accommodation.

Form of construction

The form of construction is based on in situ concrete crosswalls constructed at 3.5 metre centres to form the wall separation between rooms. The 175 mm crosswalls are constructed in storey height pours using patent metal formwork.

The suspended floors consist of 60 mm thick concrete plank floors precast on site. The precast planks span between the crosswalls. Services for the floor below are located on top of the precast planks, protected in plastic services ducts or pipes. Holes are formed through the planks for the main service drops which consist primarily of electrical wiring to plugs and light sockets. Temporary propping of the plank floors is necessary at 1500-2000 mm centres prior to placing the in situ concrete structural slab.

A feature of French construction is the extensive amount of prefabrication work which is undertaken on site. On this project, formwork casting beds have been laid out adjacent to the tower crane location. This enables a large number of plank floors to be site precast prior to their curing and lifting into position between the crosswalls.

The outer envelope of the building is formed of 200 mm terracotta blocks which are rendered and painted externally. Internally the crosswalls and enclosure walls are lined with 60 mm and 80 mm polystyrene insulation panels. Fixing of the insulation slabs is similar to the detail previously shown for low rise housing.

Sequence of construction

Figure 3.26 indicates a layout plan of the project. Figure 3.27 illustrates a site plan showing the location of the precasting beds for the plank floors, together with the tower crane position. The sequence of construction for the cross-walls and plank floors is illustrated. The formwork system utilises storey height metal formwork which is moved into position with the tower crane. The construction sequence is shown in figure 3.28 for two of the bays of the main building frame. The insulation lining to the inner surface of the cross-walls and external wall is shown in figure 3.29. Dry lining systems of this type are used currently throughout France.

CASE STUDY - STUDENT ACCOMMODATION - NANTES

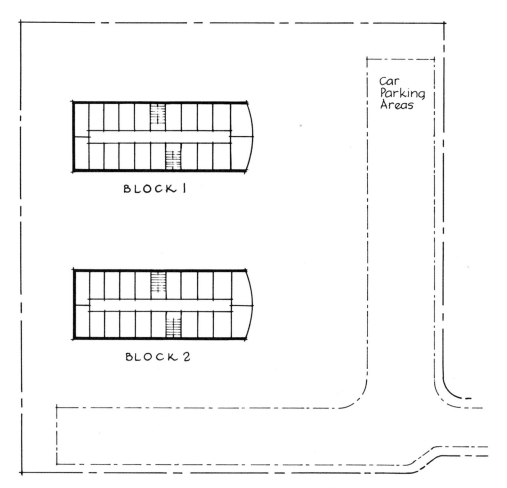

Site Location Plan

Project description

Four storey student accommodation containg eighty flats per block. The construction is based on crosswall constructed at 3·5 metre centres to form room layouts.

The concrete crosswalls are formed insitu 175mm thick with 60mm thick site precast concrete plank floors.

Figure 3.26

CASE STUDY - STUDENT ACCOMMODATION - NANTES

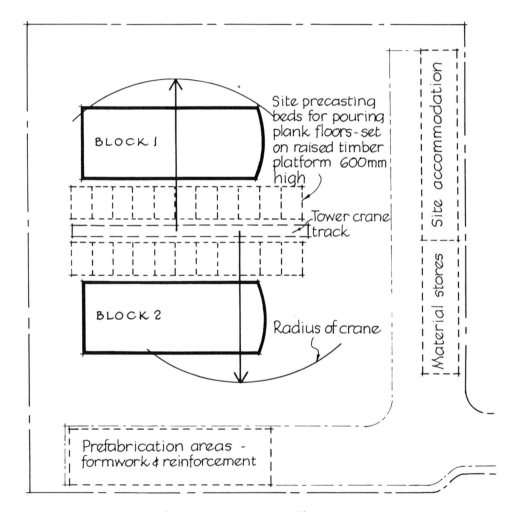

Site Layout Plan

Site precasting areas

Extensive site precasting is common practice for the production of plank floors, beams, columns, etc.

Figure 3.27

SEQUENCE OF CONSTRUCTING CROSSWALLS

Stage 1

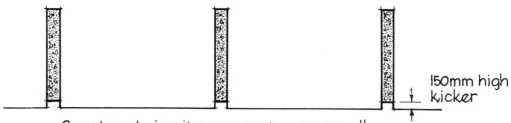

150mm high kicker

Construct in-situ concrete crosswalls on floor slab kickers. Full height pours.

Stage 2

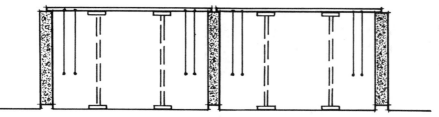

Position temporary props at 1·5 m centres and place 60mm precast concrete planks. Form holes in planks for service drops. Position service runs and drops to floor below.

Stage 3

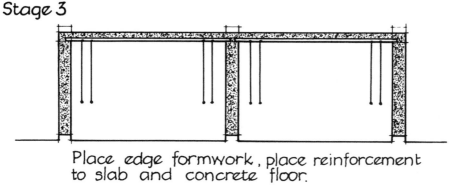

Place edge formwork, place reinforcement to slab and concrete floor.

Figure 3.28

CASE STUDY - STUDENT ACCOMMODATION - NANTES

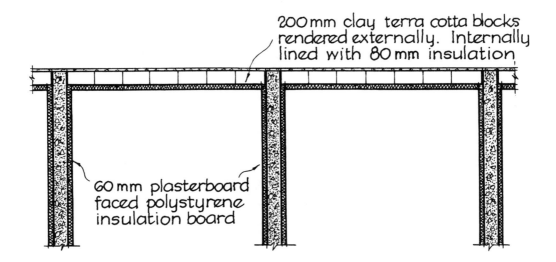

200 mm clay terra cotta blocks rendered externally. Internally lined with 80 mm insulation

60 mm plasterboard faced polystyrene insulation board

Plan of Crosswalls

Figure 3.29

4 The Construction Industry in Germany

4.1 Key information

Capital – Berlin
Area (sq. km) 356 854   Population 79.75m (1991)

German reunification officially took place on 3 October 1990 when the German Democratic Republic of the East joined the Federal Republic of Germany in the West. Data relating to construction output, prices and construction industry reviewed relate to West Germany only.

4.2 Construction output (1990) (West Germany only)

Data obtained from the Euroconstruct Conference Report – June 1991

	ECU (Billion)
New residential construction	31.60
Private non-residential construction	24.50
(offices, industrial and commercial)	
Public non-residential construction	6.00
(Schools, universities, hospitals)	
New civil engineering works	22.10
Renovation in civil engineering	9.50
Renovation and modernisation in residential property	33.00
Non-residential renovation	16.30
Total	143.00

Current prices – 1 ECU = DM 1.955 (1990 average)

Total employed in construction 1 846 000 (1988)

Building prices – labour and materials

Key labour rates for labourers and craft operatives engaged in the construction industry are shown below. A range of key material prices is also given so that comparisons may be made between each country.

Labour rate	Basic rate (per hour)		All in rate (per hour)
Unskilled labour	£8.15 (DM 19)		£20.39 (DM 45)
Craft operatives	£9.79 (DM 22)		£23.65 (DM 48)

Material rates	Unit	DM	£
High yield steel (reinforcement)	Tonne	900	367
Structural steel	Tonne	1100	449
Ordinary cement	Tonne	240	98
Carcasing timber	Cubic metre	900	367
Clay bricks	1000	–	–
100 mm Concrete blocks	Square metre	13	5.30

Apartments (multi-storey)	Square metre	DM	£
	Range low	2700	1102
	high	3000	1224

Factory units	Square metre		
	Range low	1650	673
	high	2000	816
High technology buildings	Square metre		
	Range low	5600	2285
	high	5900	2408

Value Added Tax (1993)	General level	15%
	Building rate	15%

Data obtained from *Building*, 22 January 1993. Procurement - European Costings

4.3 Review of the construction industry

Construction output in West Germany in 1990 totalled around 143 billion ECU. This results in a construction market turnover which is some 110% larger than the United Kingdom.

The pie chart in figure 4.1 indicates the division of work into the main construction categories. Work of a civil engineering nature accounts for 22% of the market. This compares with some 10.6% in the United Kingdom. A comparison of the value of work undertaken in civil engineering is as follows:

Civil Engineering (1990 figures) – billions ECU

	FDG	UK	
New work	22.1	7.6	West Germany only
Renovation/repair	9.5	2.8	

The number of contractors and the numbers of employees in relationship to the size of the company are shown in the table below (1987 figures).

Number of employees	Contracting firms	Category
Up to 19	48294	Small (up to 19)
20 to 49	6980	
50 to 99	2320	Medium (20 to 199)
100 to 199	990	
200 to 499	36	
Over 500	84	Large (over 200)
Total number of firms	58704	

Major contracting organisations in West Germany include:

Phillip Holzmann	Ed Zublin
Hochtief	Walter Thosti Boswau
Bilfinger Berger	Lurgi
Strabag Bau	Mannesmann Anlagenbau
Dykerhoff & Widmann	Wayss & Freytag

DIVISION OF CONSTRUCTION OUTPUT

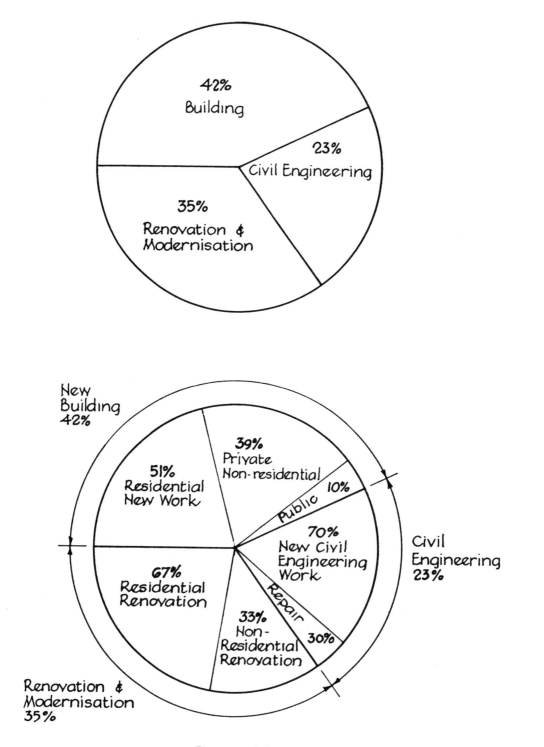

Figure 4.1

Ownership of the major companies is via a network of shareholdings with the banks and financial institutions. There are often sizeable family shareholdings in the medium sized companies which tend to operate locally and regionally.

4.4 Extent of regionalisation

The Länder/State system

The Federal Democratic Republic of Germany is divided into sixteen states, or Länder. Each state varies in both size and population. Figure 4.2 illustrates the division of the country into the sixteen states.

Each state has its own Parliament and Constitution and each makes its own regulations relating to construction and planning. The states are further divided into communes which number approximately 8500. Each commune is a corporate entity which makes its own decisions in respect of building planning, local facilities and transport.

As a consequence of the state system, building contractors, with the exception of the larger firms, tend to concentrate their activities within each state or commune. Many of the larger firms have regional offices. The majority of contractors fall into the small category (employing from 1-19 employees) and tend to be highly localised (48,294 firms).

While the state exercises general control over internal affairs, economy, finance, transport, planning and control of development, operations at local level are controlled by communes into which the states are divided.

4.5 The housebuilding industry

German clients demand a high quality of building. This has its origins in several factors: important among these is the quality of life enjoyed as a result of the education and training obtained at both professional and craft level. Architects, engineers and contractors can talk to each other and each tries to understand the other's technical problems. Education and the training of craft operatives is financed entirely by the industry. The. terms *Architekt* and *Diplom Ingenieur* are legally protected names. A German craft operative, managing his own business, must be registered and to be so must have passed associated tests and examinations. Craft operatives undertake a three year craft apprenticeship followed by a further 5 years of experience in the industry. This is followed by a 1 to 2 year programme of part-time education before obtaining a master craft operatives certificate.

GERMANY

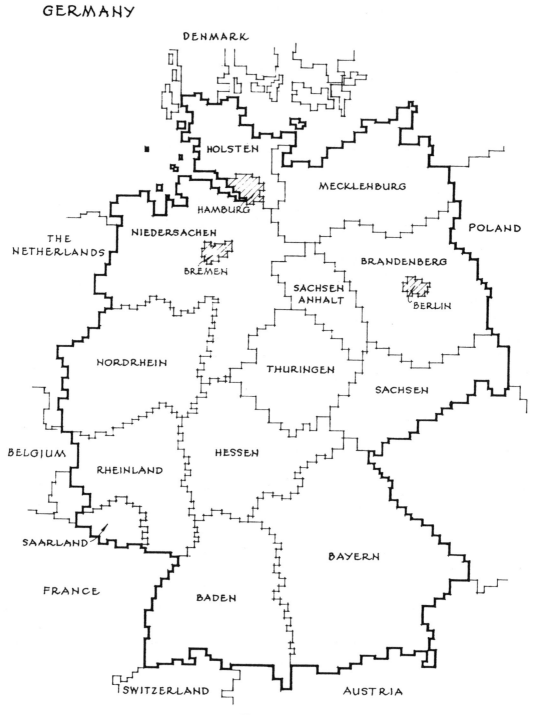

Figure 4.2

German contractors undertake housebuilding and commercial property projects but rarely undertake development risk. Speculative housebuilders of a size comparable to Tarmac, Wimpey or Barratt do not exist.

Housebuilding is mainly undertaken by small local builders within each commune. The developer sells off planned layouts with the purchaser undertaking a series of stage payments. This results in the developer/builder requiring considerably less finance than a comparable builder in the United Kingdom.

Average house prices tend to be about twice those in the UK, although even when allowance is made for the differing salary levels between the two countries, prices are still considered high. Costs are also influenced by climatic conditions and the need for higher insulation values. Speculative building is not unknown, but is not common. Where it does occur, it is on a local basis and in small developments with the majority of houses being built by small builders.

Observations on the housing market in the Cologne region

Social and rented accommodation

The suburbs of Cologne contain extensive areas of medium rise social housing. These consist mainly of four to six storey blocks with simple gabled tiled roofs. Housing designs are simply box-shaped units set out in gardened squares which are well landscaped and serviced by local shops within each complex.

Construction techniques are based on loadbearing external walls supporting in situ concrete floors. Extensive reinforced concrete basements are incorporated in order to provide parking accommodation. There is evidence in the region of an extensive building programme of constructing 5-6 storey high housing complexes.

Residential housing construction

A number of speculative residential projects were visited in the Münchengladbach and Cologne regions. The projects were being undertaken by local medium sized contractor/developers using private or in-house architects. Housing contracts involved constructing between ten and twenty units incorporating two or three varying house designs. Sales information was well presented and contained accurate assessments of building floor areas together with a concise outline specification.

Forms of construction

All house designs incorporated a basement area whether the style be detached, semi-detached or linked terraced units. Access to the basement area was provided by both an internal and an external staircase.

The basement allowed for the provision of a boiler room, garden store, workroom or hobby room.

Basement walls are constructed of 300 mm thick reinforced concrete walls which are externally waterproofed and rendered. Alternatively walls may be constructed of 300 mm thick dense sand lime blocks.

External walls are constructed 355 mm in thickness and consist of a 200 mm dense concrete inner block wall, 55 mm cavity incorporating 40 mm rockwool insulation and external facing bricks. External windows are double glazed in PVCu frames.

Suspended floors at ground floor, first floor and roof level (first floor ceiling) are constructed of 150 mm thick in situ concrete. As in The Netherlands, extensive use is made of the roof space to form a habitable room. A recent trend is the introduction of 50 mm precast concrete plank floors similar to the floor construction used in The Netherlands and France.

Roof construction is of timber rafters at 500 mm centres and exposed purlins within the bedrooms to form a feature. Extensive use is made of dormers in both two and three storey houses. Roofs are finished in concrete or clay tiles.

Construction work is highly mechanised. Mobile track mounted tower cranes dedicated to serving three to four house units were being widely used. Cranes were used for the handling of materials during the basement construction, handling blocks, in situ and precast concrete units and roofing components.

Houses are constructed to a high specification with the emphasis on quality finishes which are clearly reflected in the prices.

House prices in the speculative market

Typical prices in 1992 for detached and semi-detached properties were in the range of DM 2400 to DM 3500 per square metre of floor area. This is dependent upon the region and specification level. A house with a floor area of 120m² costs between DM 288 000 and DM 420 000. Residential flats in the inner city suburbs were available in the following price ranges:

Floor area	Price DM	Price £	
66 m²	154 000	64 166	
70 m²	170 000	70 833	Average 1991 prices
90 m²	208 000	86 666	

As in most European countries prices vary according to the location of the property, quality, site and market conditions.

Home ownership and subsidised housing

In Germany, owner occupation is less common than in the UK. The majority of tenants rent from private landlords or live in subsidised housing. In recent years the construction of flats for rented accommodation has accounted for 50% of all new houses constructed – this compares with some 20% for similar rented accommodation in the UK.

4.6 Relationships within the construction industry

The traditional trade contract system

The division of the country into states has resulted in construction activity being widely spread throughout the country.

The majority of projects are relatively small in size and value and are constructed using the traditional trade contract system as shown in figure 4.3. Each of the trade contractors has a contract with the client and all work on site is co-ordinated by the architect. The client also has a contract with the architect to cover his professional services which also *includes* the fee for the consulting engineer.

Figure 4.4 illustrates the contractual situation where a main contractor has been engaged to complete the main building shell i.e. foundations, external walls and roof. Individual specialist trade contractors are then brought in to complete the building finishes. The client has a contract with the main contractor plus separate contracts with each of the specialist sub-contractors. Co-ordination of the work is undertaken by the architect. Alternatively a trade or a general contractor may be employed to undertake the complete project.

4.7 Role of the architect

In Germany the designation architect is protected by law. Architects undertake a four to six year degree course at a recognised university or *Technische Hochschule*. On completion of the course the student is awarded a Diploma in Architecture. At this stage the person is regarded as professionally qualified and must register with the Federal Chamber of Architects in order to practice.

TRADE CONTRACT ARRANGEMENT
FOR SMALL - MEDIUM CONTRACTS

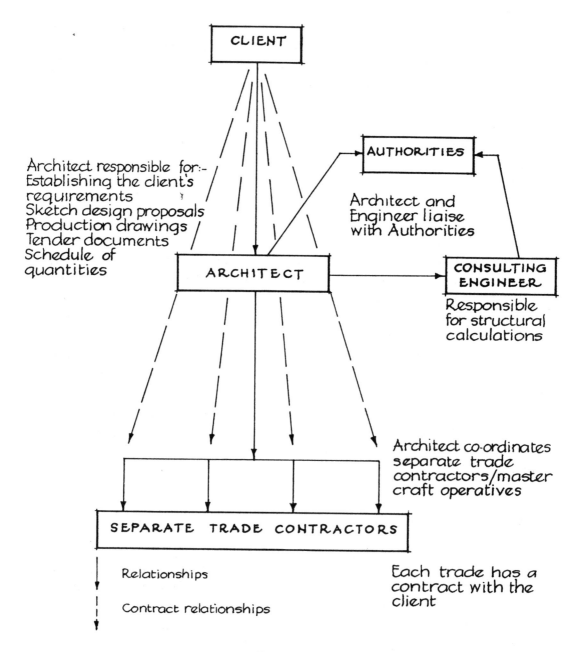

Architect responsible for:-
Establishing the client's
requirements
Sketch design proposals
Production drawings
Tender documents
Schedule of
quantities

Architect and
Engineer liaise
with Authorities

Responsible
for structural
calculations

Architect co-ordinates
separate trade
contractors/master
craft operatives

Relationships

Contract relationships

Each trade has a
contract with the
client

Figure 4.3

MAIN CONTRACTOR/SEPARATE TRADES CONTRACTUAL ARRANGEMENTS

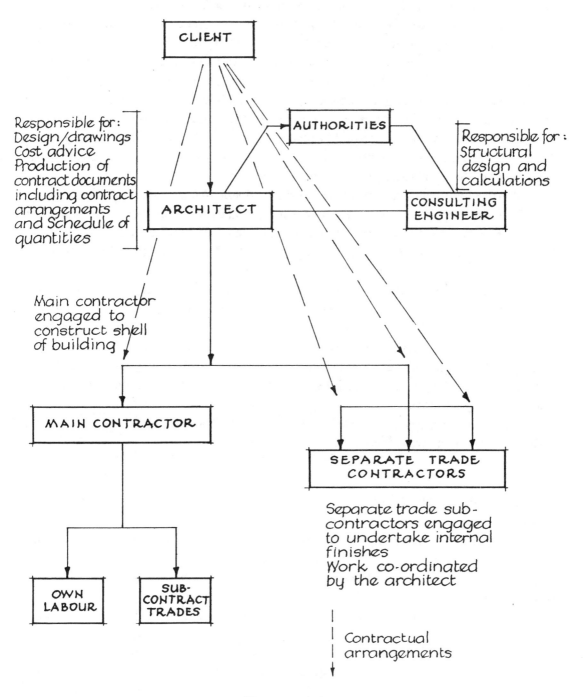

Figure 4.4

Each state has its own Architect's Chamber which is responsible for establishing legislation in order to govern the profession. It is necessary for architects to register separately in the State Chamber of the district in which they are to practice. Practices are generally small. The majority (71%) employ up to two staff. Where an architect wishes to be engaged in the public sector, an additional year's programme of professional competence is required to be undertaken. This culminates in a public examination after which, upon passing, the architect is entitled to use the title of Assessor.

In practice only architects or engineers may apply for and be granted a building permit. Architects are generally appointed directly by the client. The architect provides a complete design and specification service for the proposed building. His main function is to co-ordinate the work of the design team and supervise the construction work. Architects traditionally have a wider responsibility than their UK counterparts. Their role embraces design and production of working drawings. Their service also include cost advice, budgeting and the production of tender documentation.

Under the VOB contract (*Verdingungsordnung für Bauleitungen Vertrag* – see section 4.10.5) the architect is responsible for preparing schedules of quantities for the contractors to price. The method of measurement is in accordance with Part C, clause 32 of the VOB. The measurement rules are fully explained in the VOB IM BILD (13th Edition 1993), by R. Franz and W. Stern, published by Müller Bauverlag.

Fee scales together with the rights and responsibilities are described in the HOAI (*Honorarordnung für Architekten und Ingenieure*), the fee scale for architects and engineers. This fixes the payments for architects' services and distinguishes between basic and specific services. Basic services include taking the client's brief, developing the scheme and finalising tender arrangements. The professional services follow a similar pattern to the RIBA Plan of Work with the exception that the architects also undertake the role of quantity surveyor.

Fee competition does not exist between the 60 000 architects registered with the Federal Chamber of Architects.

4.8　Role of the engineer

In Germany the designation *Diplom Ingenieur* is protected by law in the same way as for the architect. Engineers undertake a four to six year degree course at a University, *Fachhochschule* or *Technische Hochschule* (Technical High School). On completion of the course the student is awarded a degree in engineering (Dipl-Ing).

Courses for engineers at a *Universität* are of a more academic and theoretical nature and students undertake specialisms during the final two years of the course.

Courses for engineers at the *Fachhochschule* are of a less academic nature and provide a broad more practically based engineering education. The engineer is equipped to work for a contractor or architect in both the measurement and estimating of construction work. Having achieved the diploma level he may practice as an engineer.

The engineer normally joins either a consultancy organisation (of which there are approximately 10 000 practices), a public authority or contracting organisation.

The consultancy organisations are controlled by either the VDI (German Association of Industrial Consulting Engineering Firms), or the VBI (Association of Consulting Engineering Firms).

Fee scales for engineering services are again laid down by the HOAI document in a similar way to the architect's fees. The civil/structural engineering professions is highly regarded and well respected internationally owing to its high professional standards.

Generally, only two professions are recognised in the German construction industry: architects and engineers. Registered architects and engineers may apply for and be granted a building permit. The task of the professional engineer is more concerned with public works for which no formal building permit is required.

The client is responsible for appointing both the architect and engineer. The engineer on the smaller project is responsible for providing a structural design and drawing service to the architect. On the larger projects, involving say the construction of a steel or concrete frame, his responsibility may involve both design and supervision of the works. On a public works or major engineering project however he will act as the project leader engaging an architect to undertake conceptual design only.

Proposals for the recognition of qualifications between Germany and the United Kingdom

The German VDI (*Verein Deutscher Ingenieure*) has attempted to compare qualifications between those in Germany and the UK. An extract from the comparison is as follows:

Deutsch	English
Ingenieur	Engineer. Professional designation for High-level Engineer in Germany, protected by law.
Diplom-Ingenieur	Academic and professional title for an Engineer acquired by an engineering education in both types of Hochschule: Universität and Fachhochschule, in Germany. Comparable with a Chartered Engineer in the UK.
Techniker	An Engineer's academic and professional title acquired by an engineering education at a Technische Fachschule in Germany. Comparable with an Incorporated Engineer in the UK.

Facharbeiter   Technician; a designation for professionals who have completed dual type professional education and training (*Duale Ausbildung*) in Germany. Comparable with Engineering Technician in the UK.

The term *Hochschule* in Germany relates to a university of which there are two types – *Universität*, and *Fachhochschule*.

Universität   A university which offers a more theoretical and science based education for *Ingenieure*.

Fachhochschule   A university-type college in Germany that offers a more application based education for *Ingenieure*.

4.9 Role of the quantity surveyor

The quantity surveying function is performed either by the architect or consulting engineer as part of their professional service. The role of the quantity surveyor as a separate profession is unknown in the German Republic. Separate surveying services are, however, being undertaken by a number of UK practices on major projects as the importance of the cost control function becomes more apparent on a project.

The fee scales and duties are outlined in detail in the HOAI document. Basic services include certain quantity surveying roles, such as preliminary planning, estimates of cost and checking tenders. Special architectural services which are paid for by an additional fee include the preparation of financial plans, cost analysis and control and cost surveys. The fee scales are legally enforceable and not subject to negotiation.

On international projects, a quantity surveyor may be appointed – in these cases the fee for the surveying services forms part of the architect's or engineer's fee.

An Association of German Technical Economists has been established which is a relatively new field in Germany. The technical economist's work broadly covers work measurement, costs in use and cost benefit analysis.

4.10 Contractual arrangements and building procurement

The various methods of procuring construction work are:
a) trade contract system
b) joint venture arrangement
c) main contractor/design and build

4.10.1 Trade contract system

The majority of projects undertaken are relatively small in size and value and are constructed using the trade contract system as previously shown in figure 4.3. The client enters into separate contracts with each specialist firm or sub-contractor. This arrangement is similar to the lots separes system used in France. A relatively simple building project may involve up to twenty trade contractors and hence twenty separate contracts with the client. The architect is responsible for co-ordinating the work of the trade contractors to ensure the project is completed within the contract period.

Large-scale works may be divided into lots and contracts awarded on a lot by lot basis. Alternatively, trades may be combined into lots and let as one award. The form of contract used may be the BGB Contract (*Bürgerliches Gesetzbuch Vertrag*). Alternatively, the VOB-Contract (*Verdingungsordnung für Bauleistungen Vertrag*), may be applied. This is a specific form of contract which relates to building or civil engineering works. Special conditions may be appended to the contract in relation to project completion dates and damages for non-completion. Under the terms of the VOB, the contractor's liability covers a two-year period after completion of the works. The Federal State authorities favour the use of the VOB contract and persuade clients to do so. (See notes on overall contents of VOB).

4.10.2 Joint venture arrangements

It is common practice for the larger contracting firms to undertake joint venture projects on a wide range of contracts. This assists in spreading the contractual risk and enables the medium and smaller sized contractors to participate in the work.

On a major project this may involve one contractor being responsible for the frame construction whilst another is responsible for the cladding work. Figure 4.5 illustrates the contractual relationships between the parties.

Specialist finishes contractors and services companies may also be involved in a joint venture project. The specific use of 'nominated sub-contractors' is unknown in Germany as the specialist trades quote on the same basis as normal sub-contractors.

RELATIONSHIPS ON A JOINT VENTURE PROJECT

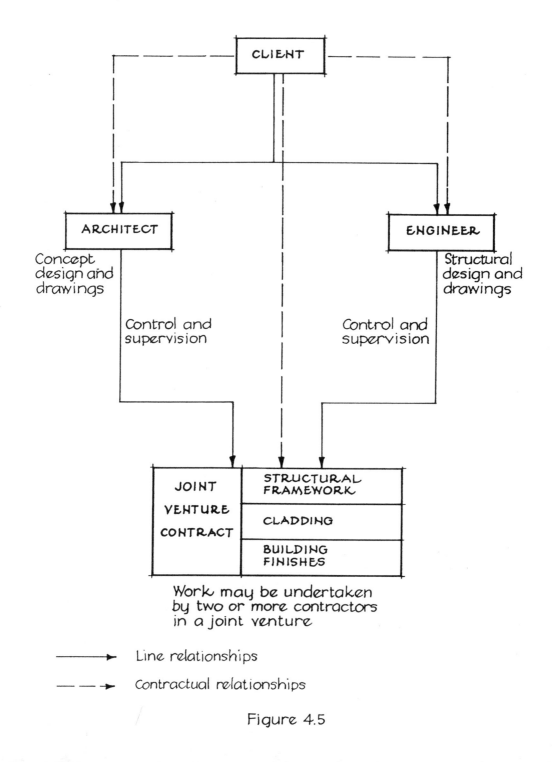

Figure 4.5

4.10.3 Other arrangements – Main contracting, Design and Build projects

The complexity of modern buildings often requires the construction skills and co-ordination requirements which necessitate the appointment of a main contractor or general contractor. Complex projects require a team approach with the architect concentrating on the design and detail. Modern buildings may also requires a greater contractor design input. This has led to the development of design and build specialists in the industrial building field. Work is undertaken on a lump sum or measurement contract basis and within a fixed time period – the time and cost risk being wholly taken by the contractor.

4.10.4 Tendering arrangements

Tendering arrangements are similar to those in the UK. Invitations to tender may be open, selective or by direct negotiation. Selective invitations must be obtained where the proposed work can by its nature can only be properly executed by a limited number of contractors. Negotiated contracts may be awarded, where for certain reasons, the work can only be executed by one contractor. Work of an extremely urgent nature may also be undertaken by direct negotiation.

Tenders for contracts may be based on specifications and bills of quantities produced by the architect, engineer or on performance specification data. Performance data are based on an outline scheme design provided by the architect. The contractor and sub-contractors are responsible for producing full working and shop drawings. The bidder is required to submit a tender which covers the design and the execution of the work supplemented by a schedule of approximate quantities and prices.

4.10.5 The VOB Contract
(Verdingungsordnung für Bauleistungen Vertrag)

The VOB was first introduced in 1926 by the leading organisations representing the construction industry and administration. At that time the public sector waived their rights to introduce their own conditions of contract.

The VOB represents a compromise between all parties and describes how the interface between clients in the private, public and public utilities sectors and the contracting parties should operate.

Contracts in Germany are covered by the *Bürgerliches Gesetzbuch* (BGB) contract which is related to the civil law. This contains 2385 paragraphs of which paragraphs 637 to 657 are applicable to works of a construction nature.

As an alternative to the BGB civil law contract the VOB may be used or a free agreed contract may be drawn up (private contract terms within the scope of the civil law). It is mandatory on public works contracts to use the VOB. Section B of the VOB contract, (clauses 1 to 18), relates to the general conditions of contract for construction works. These conditions form the framework on which the contract is based but they are not enforceable by law. Figure 4.6 indicates the relationship between the legal framework of the BGB, VOB and the free agreed contract. The VOB is divided into three sections as indicated in figure 4.6.

VOB Part A – DIN 1960

Tender regulations for construction works. This contains 32 paragraphs which are developed under the 'Basic paragraph', 'A Reference Paragraph' and 'B Reference Paragraphs'. 'Basic paragraphs' relate to private sector contracts and public works contracts under 5 million ECU in value. 'Basic paragraphs' plus 'A Paragraphs' relate to contracts over 5 million ECU in value under Directive 89/440/EEC. 'Basic paragraphs' plus 'B Paragraphs' relate to works and supply contracts in Water, Energy, Transport and Telecommunications sectors which are over 5 million ECU in value under Directive 90/531/EEC.

VOB Part B – DIN 1961

Relates directly to the general conditions of contract for construction works. The various clause headings are summarised:

1. Nature and extent of the Works
2. Reimbursement Mechanisms (Payment)
3. Contract Documents, including schedule of quantities
4. Carrying out of the Works
5. Construction Period
6. Obstruction and Interruption of the works, Delays and Extension
7. Excepted Risks
8. Determination of the Contractor's Employment
9. Determination by the Contractor
10. Liability of the Contract Parties
11. Liquidated Damages
12. Taking Over (Substantial Completion)
13. Guarantees and Warranties
14. Statement
15 Daywork
16. Payment
17. Surety Bonds
18. Disputes

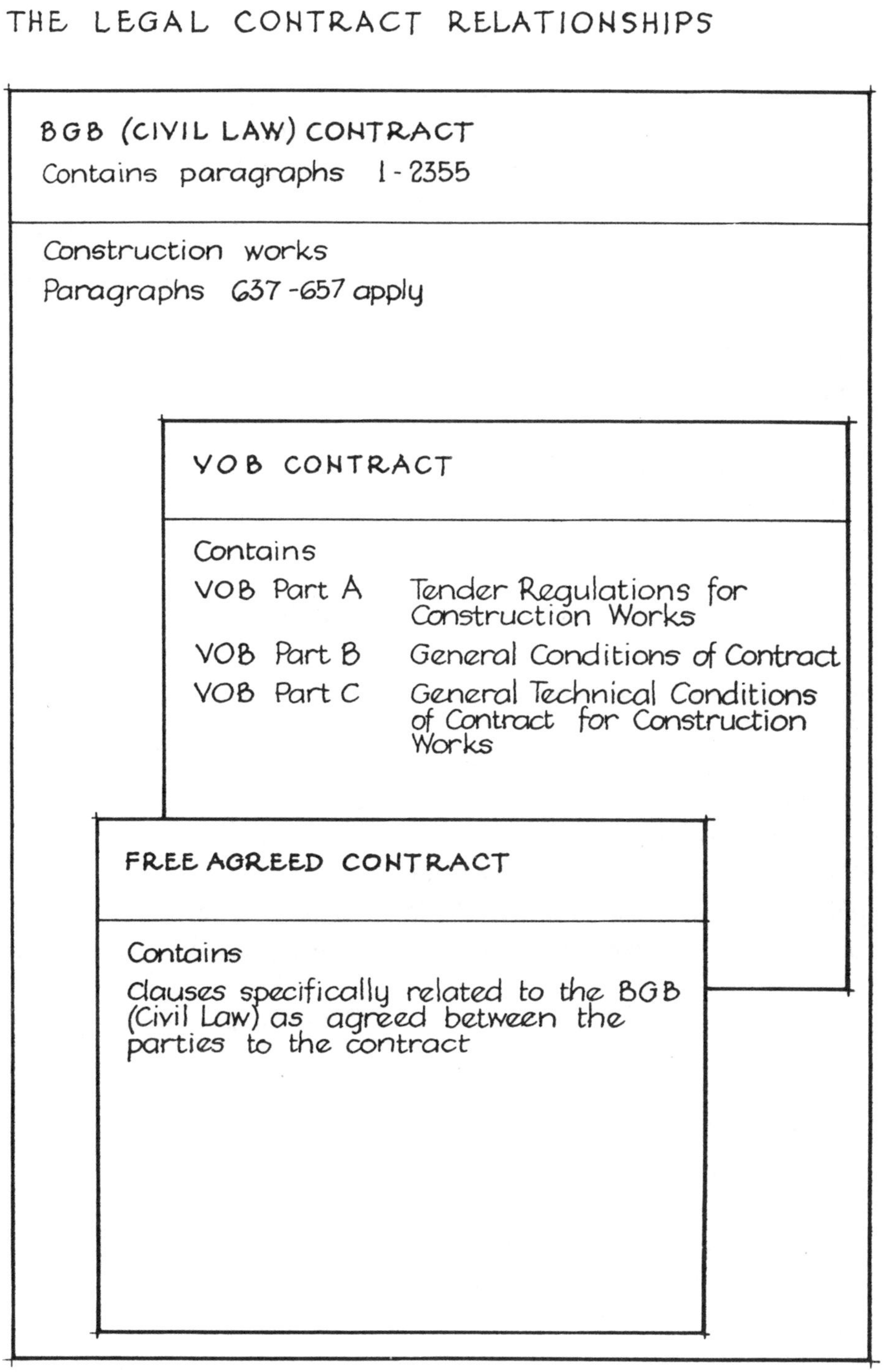

THE LEGAL CONTRACT RELATIONSHIPS

BGB (CIVIL LAW) CONTRACT
Contains paragraphs 1 - 2355

Construction works
Paragraphs 637 - 657 apply

VOB CONTRACT

Contains

VOB Part A	Tender Regulations for Construction Works
VOB Part B	General Conditions of Contract
VOB Part C	General Technical Conditions of Contract for Construction Works

FREE AGREED CONTRACT

Contains

Clauses specifically related to the BGB (Civil Law) as agreed between the parties to the contract

Figure 4.6

VOB – Part C – General Technical Conditions of Contract for Construction works

This contains a range of work items which are divided as follows:

1. General items
22. Work items relating to civil Engineering Works (DIN 18300)
32. Work items relating to Building Works (DIN18280). This contains the preparation of the schedule of quantities on which the contractors bids are based.

The six sub-sections are as follows:

0. Advisory notes relating to the description of items in the Bills of Quantities and description of works.
1. Validity of work clasification
2. Building materials
3. Execution of the works
4. Items to be included in the rates and items priced
5. Method of measurement

4.11 Planning and building control procedures

Planning requirements – Application for a development permit

The control of development is derived from Federal and Länder Building Orders and operates within the administrative courts. The relevant powers in relation to planning are based upon a written constitution. Building permission is generally allowed, but is subject to a host of regulations contained in the development permit.

A building land-use plan must be submitted as part of the development permit application. The land-use plan must clearly indicate, where relevant, the following:

(i)   Area zoned for building – both general and particular
(ii)   Public buildings
(iii)   Transport facilities
(iv)   Land for public utilisation
(v)   Green areas
(vi)   Bodies of water
(vii)   Areas for tipping,mineral extraction, etc.
(viii) Areas for agriculture and forestry
(ix)   Limits of height and mass.

Applications for development which are in accordance with the approved building land-use plan leave the authority with no alternative but to approve the application. Failure to do so may result in legal action through the administrative courts.

The granting of a development permit involves a review of the proposals under all the relevant legal requirements including planning, building regulations and infrastructure requirements. In practice the planning application is considered first, since if the proposal contradicts approved land-use plans further considerations will not be necessary.

The building permit

In the processing of an application for a building permit a wide range of formal and informal consultation takes place. A building permit can only be obtained by an architect or engineer who must certify that the application is in total conformity with the plan. Any developer can obtain copies of all previous building permits issued on a given site together with full details of proprietary land interests.

The approving authority must verify that the proposed development is in accordance with the public law. On submission of an application for a building permit there is no time limit specified regarding approval by the authority. After three months, however, an application can be made to the administrative courts on the grounds of undue delay.

When issued, a building permit is generally valid for two years. It may be extended by one year at a time. Effective control is assumed by the requirement that one set of the approved plans and one copy of the building permit are kept on site and made available on demand.

The relevant authority inspects and certifies the building works at specified stages of construction. Any operations which contravene public laws may be immediately stopped by the authority. Building works being undertaken without a building permit or deviating from the approved plans may be demolished unless lawful conditions can be verified. Substantial fines may be imposed by the courts for contravention of the building requirements.

Control and certification procedures are illustrated in figure 4.7. The *Land* provides a framework of control to ensure that the buildings do not endanger public safety, law and order, life and health. The local authorities follow rules for structural stability, thermal insulation, etc. Aspects of materials and workmanship which may affect safety are set out in a series of DIN standards.

CONTROL AND CERTIFICATION PROCEDURES

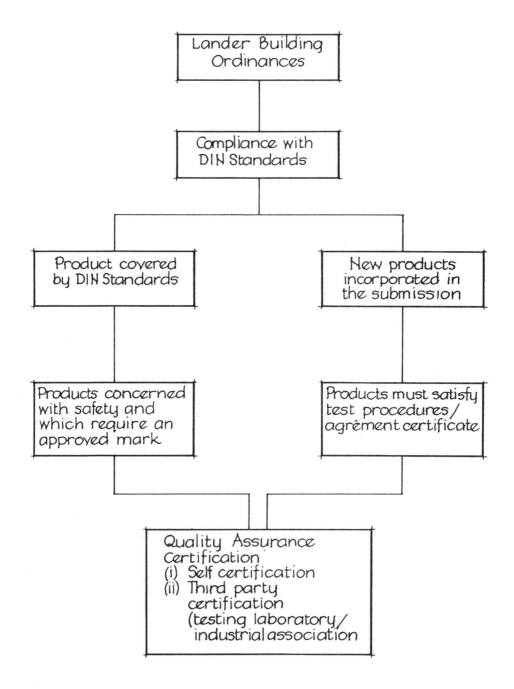

Figure 4.7

Appeals procedures

Appeals must be brought to court within one month of an application being refused. Before an appeal against an unfavourable judgement can be made against a development, the applicant must file an administrative appeal to the authority or ministerium. To bring a successful appeal it is not sufficient to show that the decision was illegal: the claimant must also establish that his legal rights as a citizen have been violated.

4.12 Low rise housing construction

Information collection

Data relating to construction techniques has been obtained from visiting contractors, developers and architect's practices. Visits to a number of residential developments has provided the data for the case studies used in the text.

The construction techniques dealt with may not be typical of building methods utilised in other regions of the country.

Form of construction

Low rise building techniques are mainly based on traditional loadbearing wall construction. The 355 mm walls support in situ concrete or precast beam and block floors.

External walls are constructed of 200 mm dense concrete blocks which form the internal wall, 50 mm insulated cavity and external facing bricks.

Internal walls are built of dense concrete blocks which are plastered on completion.

House designs normally incorporate a basement area which accommodates the boiler room, garden store and workshop. Extensive use is made of the roof space which may provide additional bedroom accommodation.

Roof construction is based on the use of timber rafters supported on purlins. Roofs are well insulated and finished with concrete tiles.

In housing construction the emphasis is on high quality finishings, e.g. doors, ironmongery, and the extensive use of ceramic tiles for floor finishes to the basement and ground floor areas.

4.13 Case study in low rise housing

4.13.1 Development layout

The layout plan in figure 4.8 illustrates the location plan of the site indicating four linked housing units and garages.

The houses contain a basement area, ground floor and first floor accommodation within the roof space. The total floor area is approximately 160 sq metres per dwelling.

It is common practice in Germany to provide a full specification to the purchaser. This indicates a summary of room sizes together with the total cubic capacity of the building.

4.13.2 House plans and elevations

Figures 4.9 to 4.11 illustrate the front elevation, floor plans and a typical cross section through the dwelling. The speculative development is located in a high class residential area of Cologne where selling prices are in the order of DM 600 000 (1992 prices).

4.13.3 Foundation and ground floor elements

Foundations consist of concrete strip footings supporting brick or dense block walls. Walls may be of solid or cavity construction between 360 mm 440 mm in thickness. Details of the foundations and ground floor construction are shown in figure 4.12 for both solid and cavity walls.

Suspended ground floor slabs over basement areas may be constructed of in situ concrete floors on smaller projects. Alternatively, precast floors incorporating a structural concrete topping may be used. Details of both solid and suspended floor construction are shown in figure 4.13, details A to C.

4.13.4 Basement wall construction

It is common practice to incorporate basements in German house construction. A section through the external wall of a dwelling from basement to roof level is shown in figure 4.14. Ventilation to the basement area is provided by means of PVC ventilator boxes with air grills at ground level. Basement walls may be constructed of 300 mm thick reinforced concrete or 360 mm dense block construction. Externally the basement wall is asphalted and protected with a layer of 50 mm thick polystyrene insulation.

LOW RISE HOUSING DESIGN

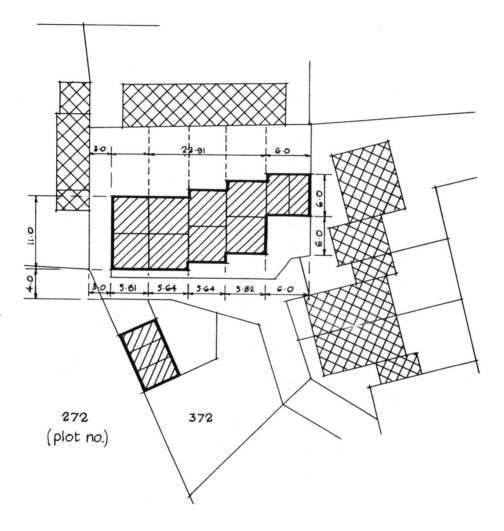

DEVELOPMENT LAYOUT PLAN

Scale 1 : 500

Figure 4.8

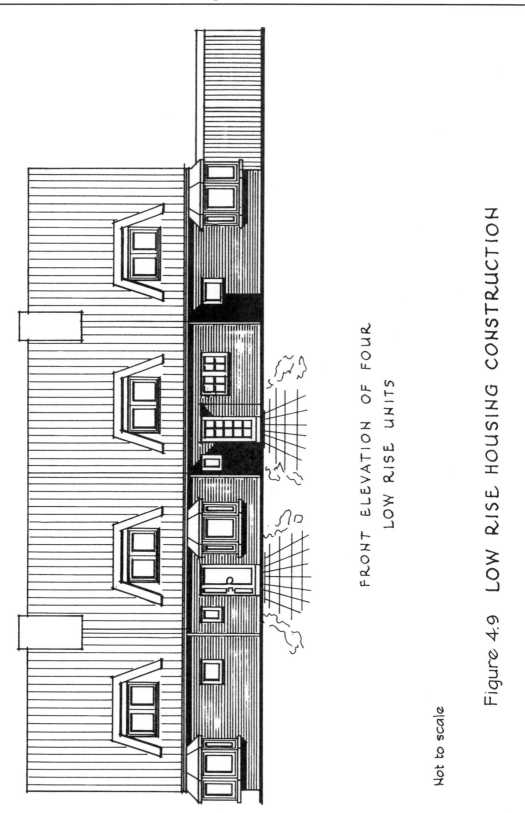

FRONT ELEVATION OF FOUR
LOW RISE UNITS

Not to scale

Figure 4.9 LOW RISE HOUSING CONSTRUCTION

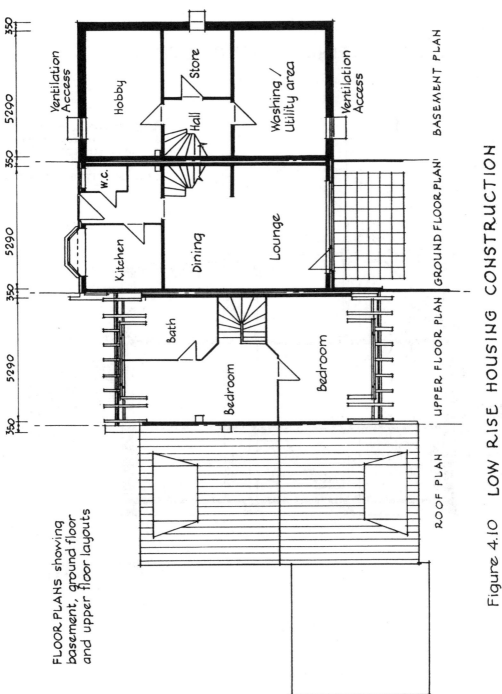

FLOOR PLANS showing basement, ground floor and upper floor layouts

Ventilation Access

Hobby

Store

Washing / Utility area

Ventilation Access

BASEMENT PLAN

Hall

w.c.

Kitchen

Dining

Lounge

GROUND FLOOR PLAN

Bath

Bedroom

Bedroom

UPPER FLOOR PLAN

ROOF PLAN

Figure 4.10 LOW RISE HOUSING CONSTRUCTION

LOW RISE HOUSING CONSTRUCTION

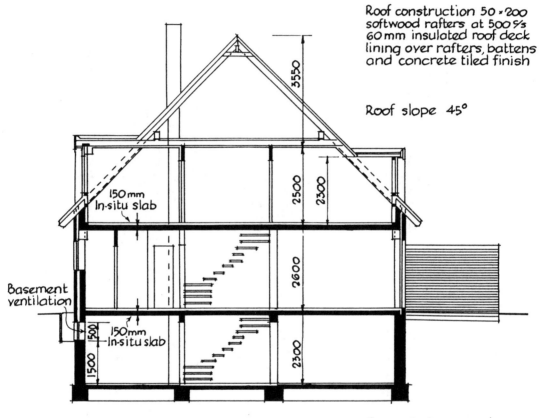

Roof construction 50 × 200
softwood rafters at 500 %
60 mm insulated roof deck
lining over rafters, battens
and concrete tiled finish

Roof slope 45°

3550

2500

2300

150 mm
In-situ slab

2600

Basement
ventilation

150 mm
In-situ slab

500

1500

2300

Concrete basement
walls with 60 mm
polystyrene lining
to walls internally

SECTION

Figure 4.11

FOUNDATION CONSTRUCTION

Detail A

External rendering

Solid ground floor

Detail B

Timber floor on battens

D.P.C.
Concrete

Fill

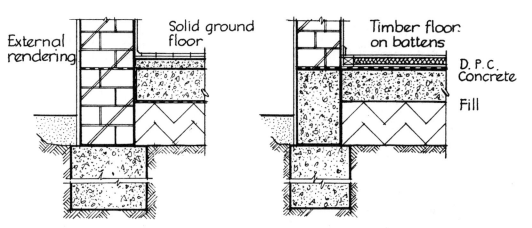

Solid wall construction

Detail C

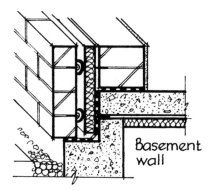

Basement wall

Detail D

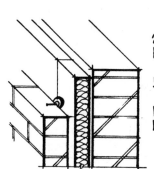

200 internal block wall

55mm insulation

110mm facing brick externally

Cavity wall construction

Foundation and ground floor details

Figure 4.12

FLOOR CONSTRUCTION

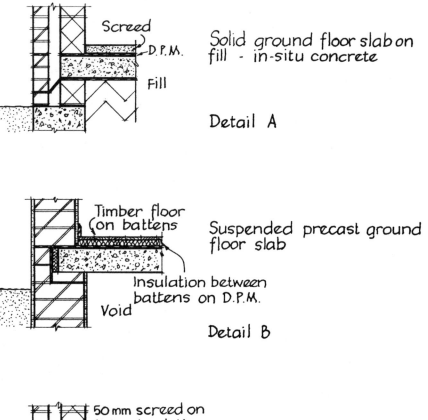

Screed
D.P.M.
Fill

Solid ground floor slab on fill - in-situ concrete

Detail A

Timber floor on battens

Suspended precast ground floor slab

Insulation between battens on D.P.M.
Void

Detail B

50 mm screed on 40 mm insulation

In-situ concrete suspended first floor slab

Detail C

Ground floor and suspended floor construction

Figure 4.13

EXTERNAL WALL CONSTRUCTION

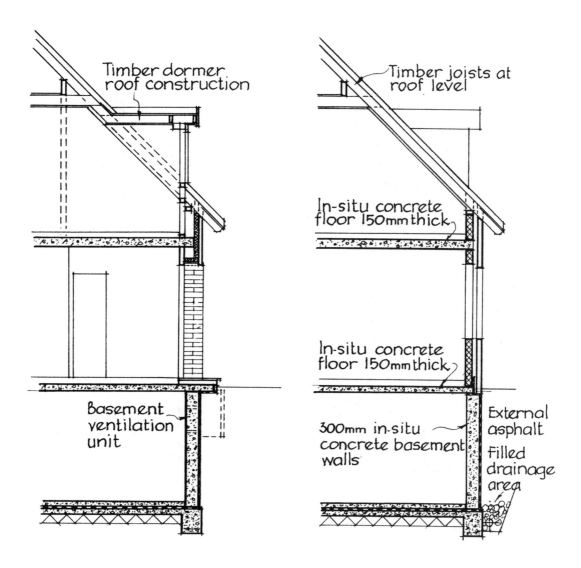

Timber dormer roof construction

Timber joists at roof level

In-situ concrete floor 150mm thick

In-situ concrete floor 150mm thick

Basement ventilation unit

300mm in-situ concrete basement walls

External asphalt

Filled drainage area

Sections through external wall

Figure 4.14

FOUNDATION CONSTRUCTION - BASEMENTS

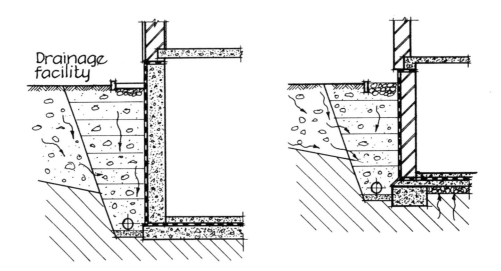

Basement wall construction

Basement wall and foundation detail

Figure 4.15

Figure 4.15 illustrates basement wall construction in concrete or blockwork indicating the provision of a drainage facility to relieve the build up of ground water pressure on the wall. Internally the basement wall may be insulated with 60 mm thick plasterboard dry lining slabs.

4.13.5 External wall construction

Various forms of external wall construction are shown in figure 4.16. The overall external wall construction may vary from a 370 mm thick solid block wall with a rendered face, through to a 440 mm thick cavity wall. This is dependent upon the specification requirements laid down by the architect. A high specification external wall element for a three storey block of residential flats is constructed as follows:

External facing brick	–	110 mm
90 mm cavity consisting of:		
fibreglass insulation	–	50 mm
polystyrene insulation	–	40 mm
Internal loadbearing wall	–	225 mm
Internal plaster	–	15 mm
Overall wall thickness		440 mm

(see figure 4.16, detail B)

The sequence of constructing the external walls of a three storey block of flats first involves constructing the 225 mm thick internal face of the external wall. As construction proceeds from floor to floor the in situ or precast floors are incorporated. Once at roof level, work continues with the roof construction. The insulation and external facing bricks are then laid from ground floor to roof level.

Safety precautions at site level with regards to the provision of external scaffolding can be rather lax on the smaller projects. The responsibilty for safety lies with the main contractor. Each contractor pays an insurance premium to cover for site safety procedures. Inspectors from the insurance companies are responsible for checking that safety levels are being maintained on site and insurance premiums are related to the contractor's safety performance.

EXTERNAL WALL CONSTRUCTION

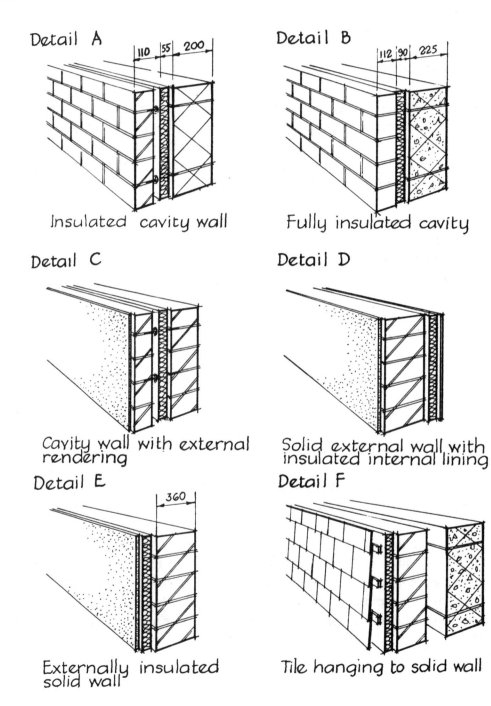

Detail A — Insulated cavity wall

Detail B — Fully insulated cavity

Detail C — Cavity wall with external rendering

Detail D — Solid external wall with insulated internal lining

Detail E — Externally insulated solid wall

Detail F — Tile hanging to solid wall

Figure 4.16

4.13.6 Suspended floor construction

Suspended floor construction varies throughout the regions. Floors may be constructed using the following methods:

1. In situ concrete floors laid 150 mm thick. The surface is finished with 40 mm insulation and 50 mm thick sand/cement screed to receive the floor finish.

2. 60 mm thick precast concrete plank floors spanning between loadbearing walls laid to act as permanent formwork. A 100 mm thick structural in situ concrete slab is then placed over to form the floor construction. Similar procedures are common in both France and the Netherlands.

3. 150 mm thick precast concrete wideslab floor units spanning between loadbearing walls.

Figure 4.17, details A to D, illustrate a variety of flooring systems.

4.13.7 Thermal insulation requirements

The thermal insulation requirements for domestic housing construction are set out in the DIN Standard 4108 (1982 Regulations). An appendix to to DIN 4108 is to be introduced in 1993 for low energy housing which takes into consideration the specification requirements of the designer.

The minimum 'U' values for walls are relative to the wall areas of the dwelling. Minimum 'U' values are also shown in the DIN standards in order to reduce the incidence of condensation in the proximity of wall and floor junctions within a dwelling.

Figure 4.18 illustrates the thermal insulation requirements for walls, roof and ground floor constructions.

4.13.8 Roof element

The roof construction on low rise housing units and three to four storey height flats is constructed using traditional timber rafters and purlin construction. Tie beams and purlins are incorporated in order to provide room areas with the roof space as shown in figure 4.19. Where rooms are formed in the roof space additional fire protection is required to be provided as detailed in figure 4.20.

FLOOR CONSTRUCTION

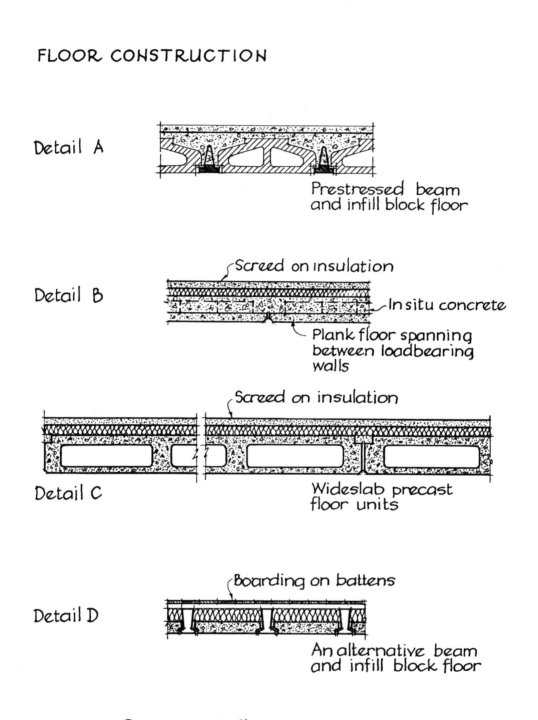

Detail A

Prestressed beam
and infill block floor

Detail B

Screed on insulation

In situ concrete

Plank floor spanning
between loadbearing
walls

Detail C

Screed on insulation

Wideslab precast
floor units

Detail D

Boarding on battens

An alternative beam
and infill block floor

Suspended floor construction

Figure 4.17

THERMAL INSULATION REQUIREMENTS ('U' VALUES)

Temperature Range   −10°C to +20°C

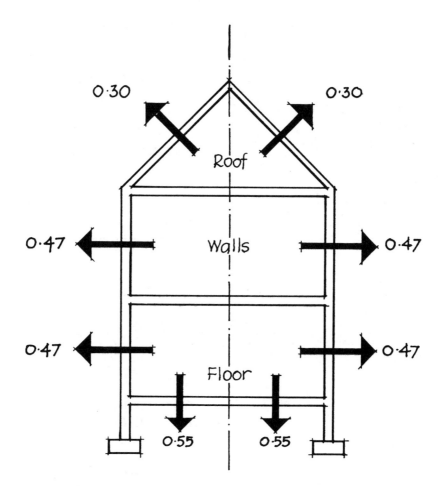

DIN Standard   4108

Figure 4.18

ROOF CONSTRUCTION

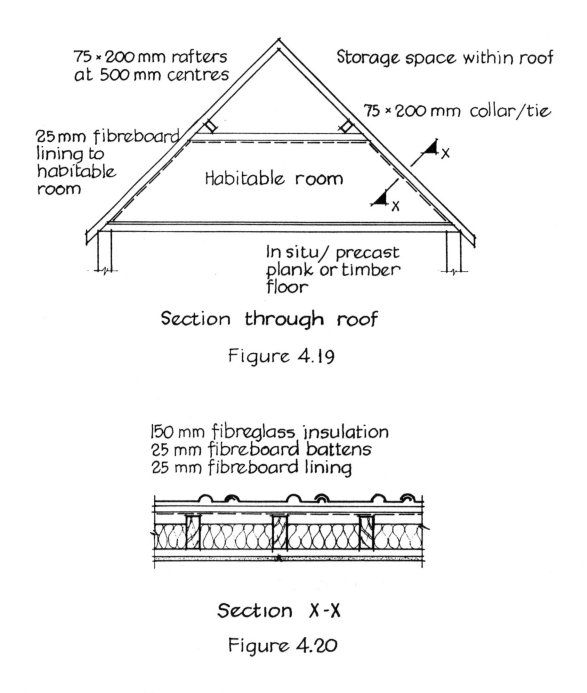

75 × 200 mm rafters at 500 mm centres

Storage space within roof

75 × 200 mm collar/tie

25 mm fibreboard lining to habitable room

Habitable room

X

X

In situ/ precast plank or timber floor

Section through roof

Figure 4.19

150 mm fibreglass insulation
25 mm fibreboard battens
25 mm fibreboard lining

Section X-X

Figure 4.20

ROOF CONSTRUCTION

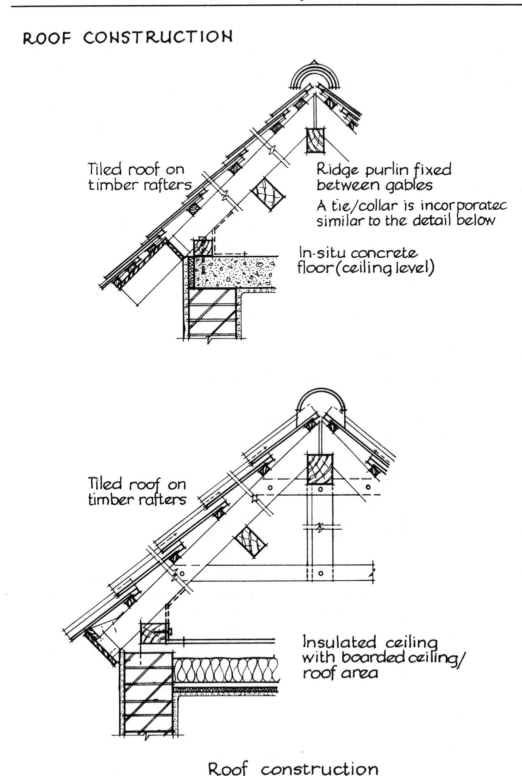

Tiled roof on
timber rafters

Ridge purlin fixed
between gables

A tie/collar is incorporatec
similar to the detail below

In·situ concrete
floor (ceiling level)

Tiled roof on
timber rafters

Insulated ceiling
with boarded ceiling/
roof area

Roof construction

Figure 4.21

Figure 4.21 illustrates traditional timber roof construction showing the strapping required to tie the roof to the external walls or in situ concrete floors. In regions such as Saxony extensive use has been made of 'Eternit' slates laid to resemble shiplap tiling.

German timber roof construction appears to be considerably over designed. Large section timbers are used for rafters, purlins and ties which adds considerably to the cost of the roof. The use of trussed rafters on housing projects was rarely seen.

4.14 Medium rise construction

Private residential flats for sale or rent may be constructed up to four or five storeys in height using loadbearing wall construction. External wall construction of cavity or solid walls may support in situ, precast plank or precast flooring units. The four-storey residential flats outlined in figure 4.31 to 4.36 are typical of the construction techniques utilised in the Cologne area.

4.15 Case study – Medium rise construction
Four-storey residential flats in Hildesheim, Lower Saxony

The project involves the construction of fifty-one flat units which will be available for rent on completion. Floor areas vary between 50 square metres to 90 square metres and provide 2, 3, or 4 rooms per unit. Rentable values on completion will be in the range of DM 15 to 25 per square metre of floor area per month.

4.15.1 Construction overview

The flats are of solid loadbearing block construction supporting precast concrete plank floors. The 360 mm thick solid block walls are rendered externally and plastered internally. Timber sloping roofs provide accommodation within the roof areas. On site car parking is provided within the basement area formed under the block.

Figure 4.22 illustrates a part elevation and section of the development proposals. A section from the basement level to the roof level is shown in figure 4.23.

4.15.2 Contractual relationships

The project is under the direct control of the architect. The full design, drawings, contract documentation and schedules of quantities have been prepared by the architect and competitive tenders obtained for the main work stages. Figure 4.24 illustrates the contractual relationships between the various contractors involved in the project.

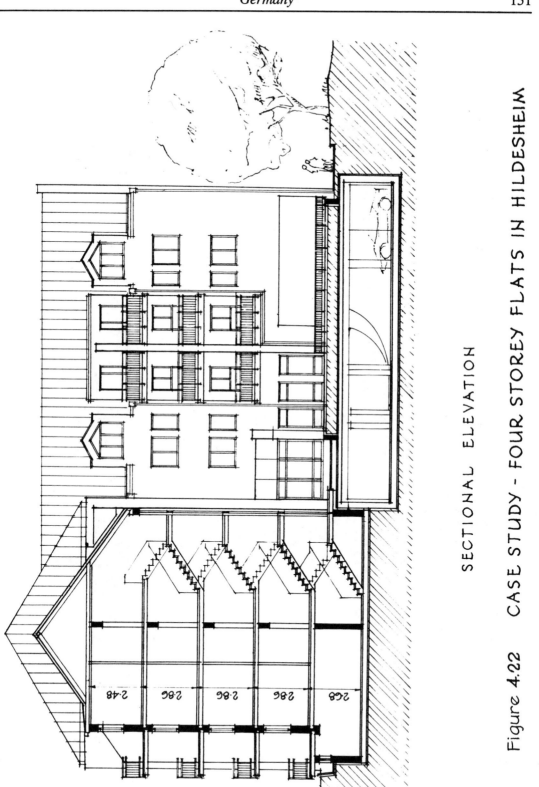

SECTIONAL ELEVATION

Figure 4.22   CASE STUDY - FOUR STOREY FLATS IN HILDESHEIM

CASE STUDY - FOUR STOREY FLATS IN HILDESHEIM

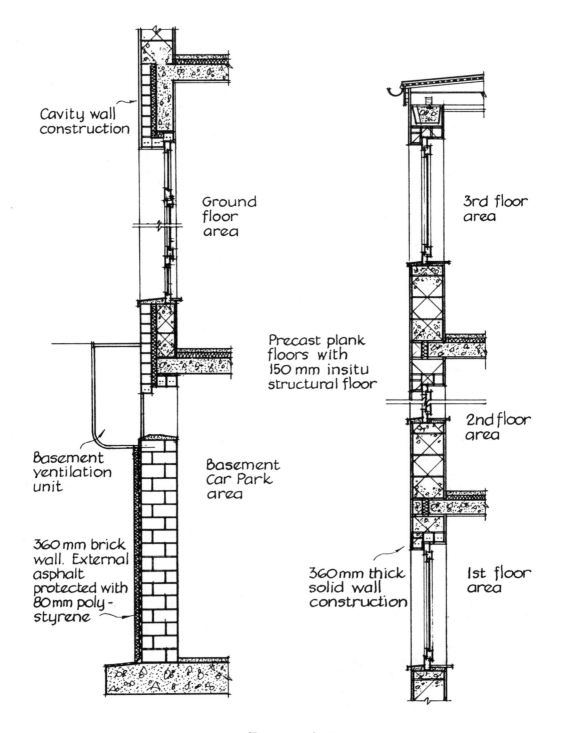

Cavity wall construction

Ground floor area

Basement ventilation unit

360 mm brick wall. External asphalt protected with 80 mm poly-styrene

Basement Car Park area

Precast plank floors with 150 mm insitu structural floor

360 mm thick solid wall construction

3rd floor area

2nd floor area

1st floor area

Figure 4.23

CONTRACTUAL RELATIONSHIPS

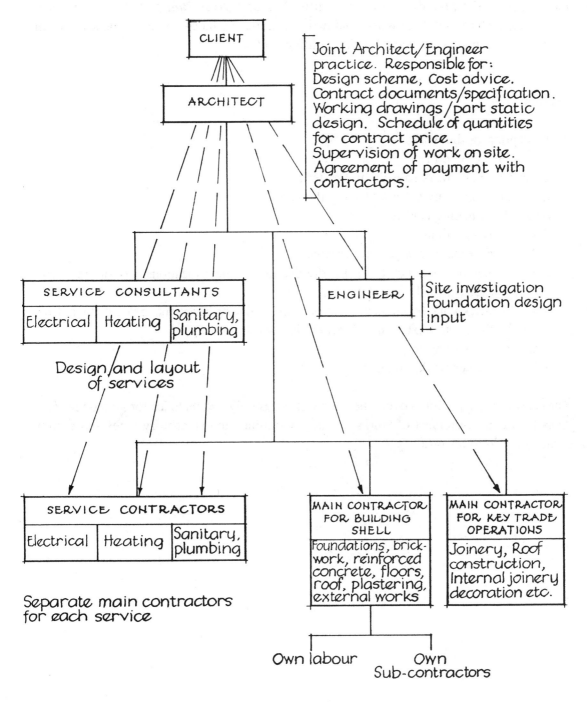

CLIENT

ARCHITECT

Joint Architect/Engineer practice. Responsible for: Design scheme, Cost advice. Contract documents/specification. Working drawings/part static design. Schedule of quantities for contract price. Supervision of work on site. Agreement of payment with contractors.

SERVICE CONSULTANTS

| Electrical | Heating | Sanitary, plumbing |

ENGINEER

Site investigation Foundation design input

Design and layout of services

SERVICE CONTRACTORS

| Electrical | Heating | Sanitary, plumbing |

MAIN CONTRACTOR FOR BUILDING SHELL

Foundations, brick-work, reinforced concrete, floors, roof, plastering, external works

MAIN CONTRACTOR FOR KEY TRADE OPERATIONS

Joinery, Roof construction, Internal joinery decoration etc.

Separate main contractors for each service

Own labour   Own Sub-contractors

Figure 4.24

Each of the main contractors has a separate contract with the client and the architect is responsible for the co-ordination of the work.

The contract has been awarded under the conditions of the VOB. Rules relating to the measurement of the building works are outlined in the *VOB im Bild* (13th Edition Müller, Bauverlag). The schedule of works and main quantities includes the following sections in relation to the main contractor for the building shell.

Section

1. Desciption of the works
2. Conditions of contract
3. Specification of workmanship and material
4. Contract preliminaries – establishing the site
5. Schedule of main quantities
   - 5.1 – Excavations
   - 5.2 – External drainage and manholes
   - 5.3 – Reinforced concrete works (divided into element locations, i.e. floors stairs, prefabricated concrete)
   - 5.4 – Brickwork (in element locations, i.e. cellar or basement, ground floor, first floor, etc., external brickwork, internal brickwork)
   - 5.5 – Insulation
   - 5.6 – Plaster works, internal, external

The schedule of quantities covers the main quantities only and includes for all labour. The rules for the measurement of works are clearly outlined in explanatory notes and sketch form in the *VOB im Bild*.

4.15.3 Case study – Speculative four-storey residential development

Project information

The project involves the construction of an infill block of flats between existing buildings. Accommodation is provided on four levels over a basement area. The basement accommodates storage and washroom facilities for the residents. Garage facilities are located at the rear of the property with access provided via a covered way at ground floor level. The form of construction is based on loadbearing walls supporting in situ concrete floors and beams. The rear of the building incorporates in situ concrete staircases and landing areas in order to provide adequate means of escape.

The basement is constructed of 300 mm thick concrete walls incorporating externally applied asphalt tanking.

External elevations are brick clad and doors and windows are of PVCu material. The flats are finished to a high specification level.

4.15.4 Plan and elevations

Figures 4.25 and 4.26 illustrate the front and rear elevations of the apartment development. Figures 4.27 to 4.29 indicate the basement plan, ground floor plan and a typical flat layout for the upper floor. Figure 4.30 shows a cross section through the building. Details in relation to the various elements of the construction are indicated for the foundations, basement, external walls and roof in section 4.13.3 and 4.13.8.

4.15.5 Plant utilisation on low-rise housing projects

Low rise housing construction is extensively mechanised with the widespread use of small tower cranes. It is not uncommon to observe 3 or 4 mobile tower cranes on a development of 30-40 house units. Extensive mechanisation is inherent in the construction process.

Cranes are utilised for the basement construction in the handling of formwork, reinforcement and concrete. The superstructure work involves the handling of prestressed floor beams, blocks and in situ concrete for columns, beams and floors.

MEDIUM RISE CONSTRUCTION

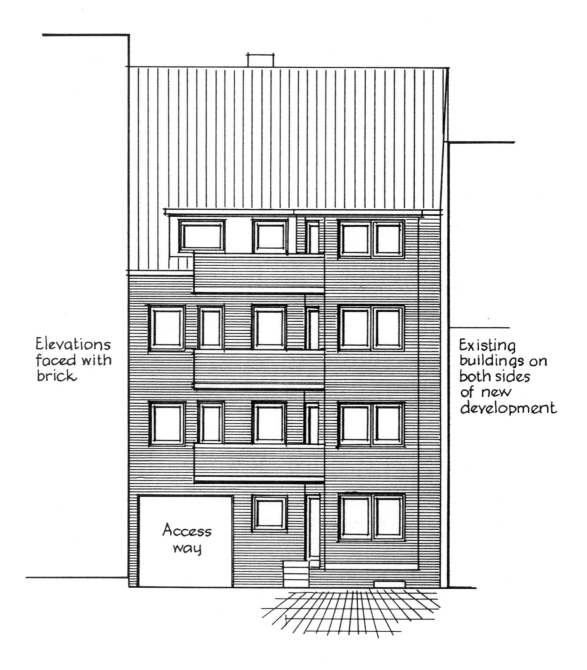

Elevations faced with brick

Existing buildings on both sides of new development

Access way

FOUR STOREY RESIDENTIAL FLATS
FRONT ELEVATION

Figure 4.25

MEDIUM RISE CONSTRUCTION

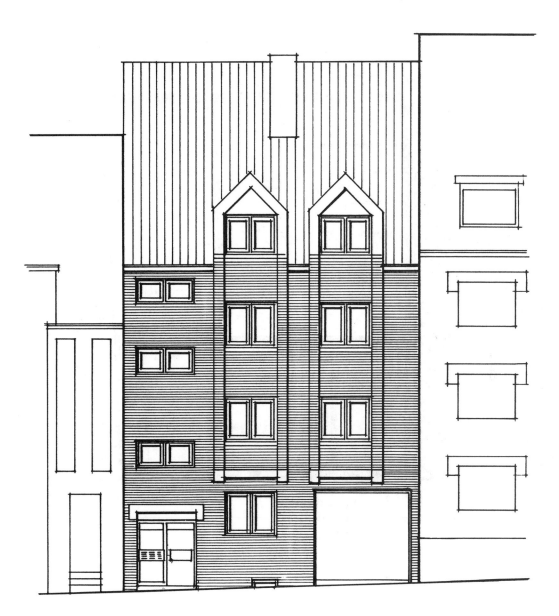

FOUR STOREY RESIDENTIAL FLATS
REAR ELEVATION

Figure 4.26

MEDIUM RISE CONSTRUCTION

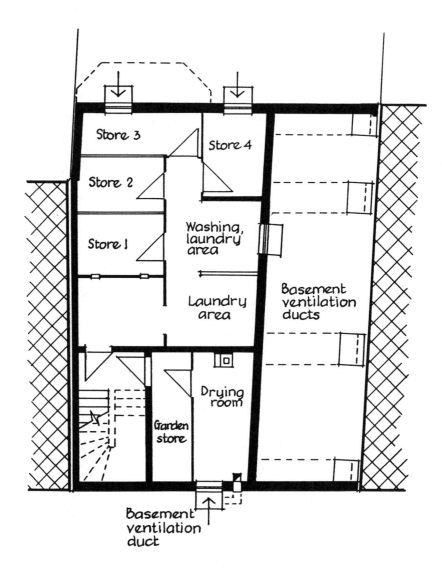

FOUR STOREY RESIDENTIAL FLATS
BASEMENT PLAN

Figure 4.27

MEDIUM RISE CONSTRUCTION

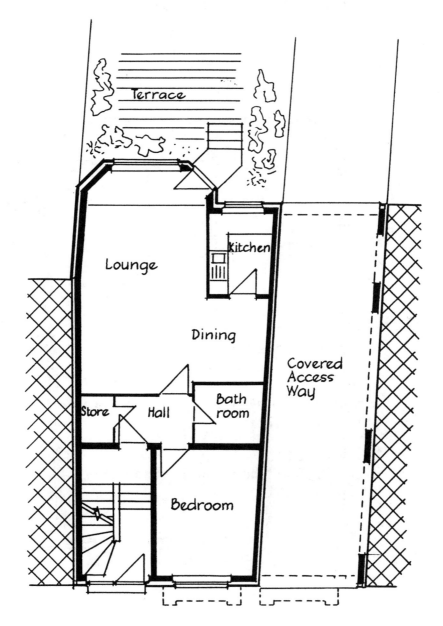

PLAN OF GROUND FLOOR UNIT

ONE BEDROOM FLAT

Figure 4.28

MEDIUM RISE CONSTRUCTION

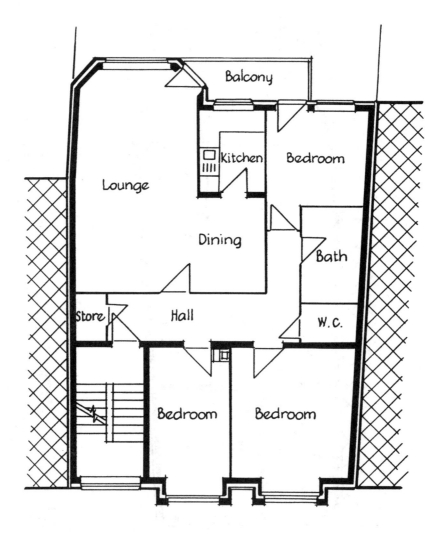

PLAN OF FIRST FLOOR UNIT
(Second and third floors similar)
THREE BEDROOM FLAT

Figure 4.29

MEDIUM RISE CONSTRUCTION

SECTION

FOUR STOREY
RESIDENTIAL
FLATS

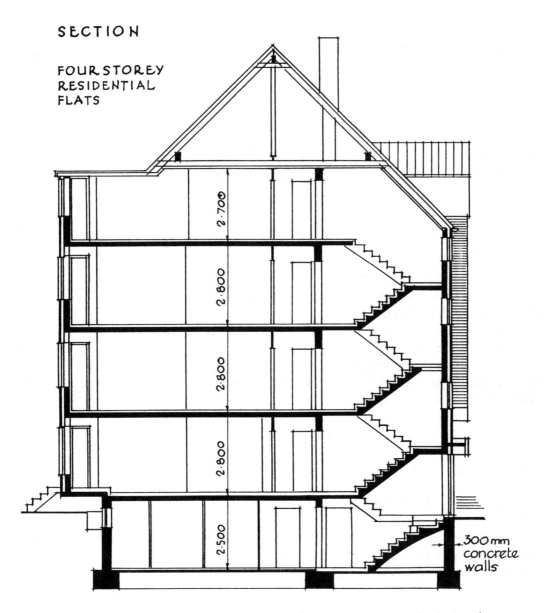

2·700

2·800

2·800

2·800

2·500

→ 300 mm
concrete
walls

Form of construction - 200 mm dense concrete block loadbearing walls supporting 150 mm thick in-situ concrete suspended
floors.
External brickwork to front and rear elevations.
In-situ concrete rear access landings and staircases

Figure 4.30

5 The Construction Industry in The Netherlands

5.1 Key information

Capital – Amsterdam
Land area (sq. km) 33 936   Population 15.13m (1992)

5.2 Construction output (1990)
Data obtained from the Euroconstruct Conference Report – June 1991.

	ECU (Billion)
New residential construction	5.48
Private non-residential construction	4.15
(offices, industrial and commercial)	
Public non-residential construction	1.22
(schools, universities, hospitals)	
New civil engineering work	2.83
Renovation in civil engineering	0.67
Renovation and modernisation in residential property	5.03
Non-residential renovation	4.93
Total	24.29

Current prices – 1 ECU = 2.32 Dfl (1990 average)

Building prices – labour and materials

The following indicates key labour rates for labourers and craftsmen engaged in the construction industry. A range of key material prices are also indicated in order that comparisons may be made between each country.

Labour rate	Basic rate (per hour) £	All-in-rate (per hour) Dfl
Unskilled labour	12.70 (35 Dfl)	£14.54 (40 Dfl)
Craftsmen	18.12 (50 Dfl)	£19.57 (54 Dfl)

Material rates	Unit	Price Dfl	£
High yield steel	tonne	1300	472
Structural steel	tonne	3000	1091
Ordinary cement	tonne	565	205
Carcasing timber	Cubic metre	236	650
Clay bricks	1000	127	350
100 mm Concrete blocks	Square metre	19	6.9

			Dfl	£
Apartment – cost per square metre	Range	Low	1100	400
		High	1600	582
Factory units – cost per sqaure metre	Range	Low	950	345
		High	1800	654

Value Added Tax rate (1993)   General level 18.5%
                               Building rate 18.5%
Data obtained from *Building*, 22 January 1993, Procurement – European costings

5.3 Review of the construction industry

Construction output in 1990 totalled 25 billion ECU. This represents about 37% of the UK market output. The pie chart in figure 5.1. indicates the division of work into three main categories:

Building work   –   45%
Building renovation –   41%
Civil engineering   –   14%

DIVISION OF CONSTRUCTION OUTPUT

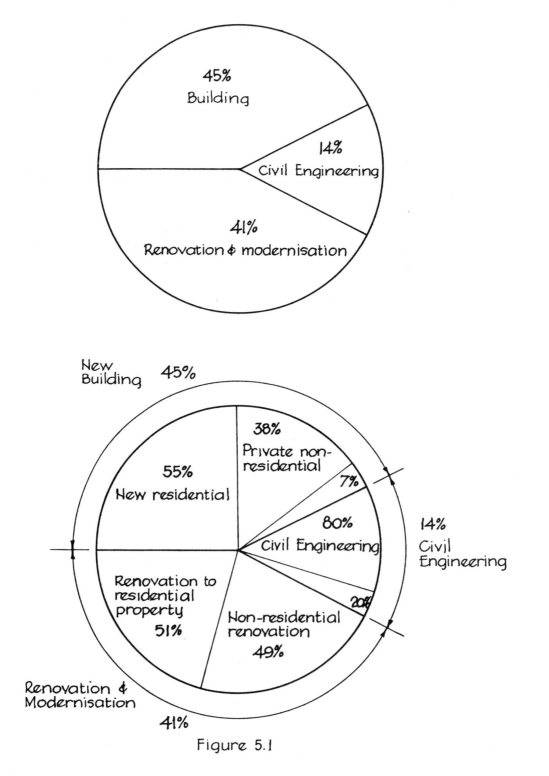

Figure 5.1

In 1988 the size of building companies categorised by numbers of employees was as follows:

Number of Employees	% of firms
1 – 10	73.2
11 – 20	13.5
21 – 50	9.1
51 – 100	2.8
> 100	1.4

Comparing these figure with companies specialising in service installations, the range is somewhat similar:

Number of employees	% of firms
1 – 9	77.2
10 – 49	19.7
> 50	3.1

(Source – Euroconstruct)

Major contracting organisations from the 1991 statistics include:

H.G.B.	Boskalis
Ballast Needam	Kondor Wessels Group
NBM – Amstelland	Dura
BAM Group	Strukton Group
Wilma International	Mourik
Ver Hejmans	Van Oorl Group.

5.4 Extent of regionalisation

The Netherlands is divided into eight provinces. These include Zeeland, North Brabant. Limburg, Gelderland, Utrecht, South Holland, North Holland, Overijssel, Friesland, Denthe and Groningen province. The majority of construction activity is in the Rotterdam and Amsterdam areas. Extensive social housing developments are under construction in North Brabant in the proximity of Breda, Tilburg and Eindhoven. Figure 5.2 illustrates a country map.

PROVINCES OF THE NETHERLANDS

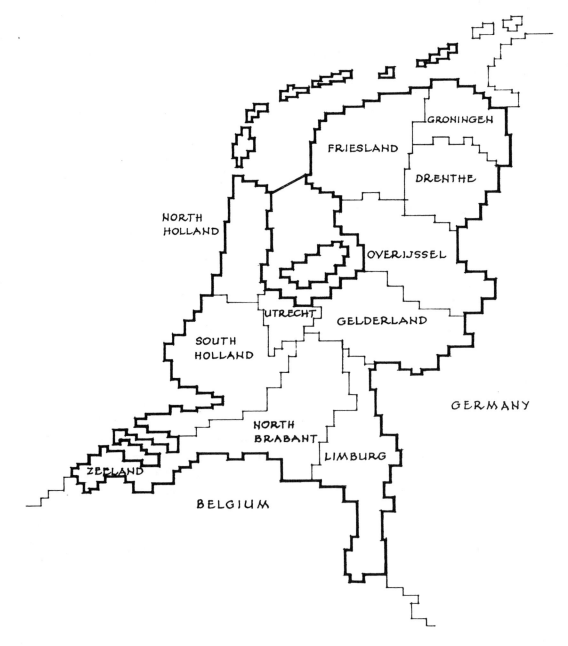

Figure 5.2

5.5 The housebuilding industry

The total number of housing completions in 1991 was 90 000 units. The number of houses constructed in the various sectors were as follows:

Subsidised housing – authority controlled	27 000
Subsidised housing – privately owned/housing associations/co-operatives	24 000
Subsidised housing for rent in the private sector	5 000
Residential speculative houses	33 000
Total houses completed	90 000

Thirty-seven per cent of the houses constructed are within the speculative sector which compares with the overall ownership percentage of 45%. The cost of rented accommodation varies from 800 to 1600 guilders per month, depending upon the number of rooms and the locality. Property prices in the Brabant region are in the following price range (1992 prices).

Type of property	Price range (guilders)	£
Terraced village or town property in need of renovation	84000-100000	30500-36360
Inner city medium rise flats, two-bedroomed accommodation built in the 1970 era	70000-110000	25450-40000
Modern inner city flats built to a high specification constructed between 1985-8	250000-350000	90900-127300
Quality detached bungalow or house, 3-4 bedroomed property	700000-900000	254500-327200

Exchange rate 1 Pound = 2.75 Dfl (1990 average)

Observations of housing projects in the Tilburg area of Brabant

A number of large residential development projects are being constructed at Reeshof and Oosterhout in the suburbs of Tilburg. The Reeshof development contains a mix of subsidised private houses similar to the housing layout as indicated in case study 5.13.8.

Crosswall construction is predominantly used as the main building system. The Reeshof project contains a wide variety of crosswall forms including in situ concrete, precast crosswalls and traditional precast walling blocks.

An interesting development project in Tilburg is the Focal Point project. This is a residential development of eighty-one linked houses. Figure 5.3 indicates a development layout plan highlighting the distinctive scheme originality. There is however a danger of road congestion around the hammer heads of the culs-de-sac and restrictive views from the kitchens. Figure 5.4 shows the ground and upper floor plans of a three-bedroomed linked unit.

5.6 Relationships within the construction industry

As in the UK, it is customary to employ a general contractor. Contracts are normally based on a brief and drawings and the contractor is responsible for assessing his own quantities and degree of contractual risk. Tenders are generally on a lump sum basis together with a schedule of prices for use in valuing variations to the contract.

The architect plays a key role in providing advice on the project feasibility, cost advice, construction advice and documentation. The services of a consulting engineer are necessary to provide advice on structural design, inspection and quality control procedures.

The contractor is responsible for insuring the building during construction and obtaining insurance to cover defects up to a period of ten years after completion of the project. The relationship between the parties involved in a project are shown in figure 5.5.

5.7 Role of the architect

Architects undertake a four-year course at a technical university (*Technische Universiteit*) in order to qualify as a practising architect. The study programme is theoretically based and practical experience is built up during the early years in practice.

DEVELOPMENT LAYOUT PLAN

Residential project of 81 linked houses

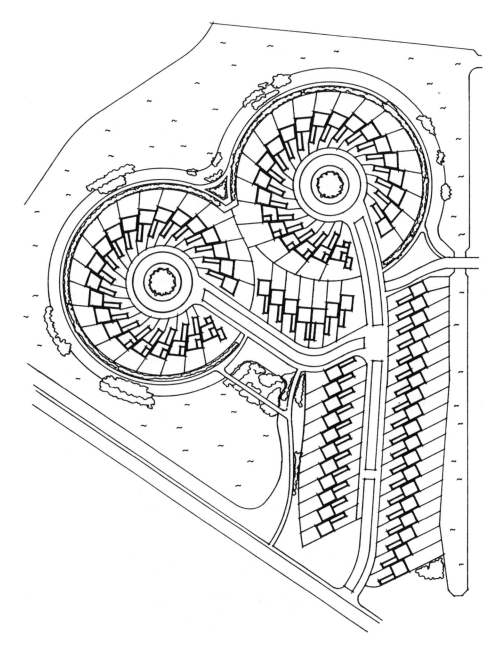

FOCAL POINT PROJECT · TILBURG · BRABANT

Figure 5.3

RESIDENTIAL PROJECT · TILBURG
FOCAL POINT

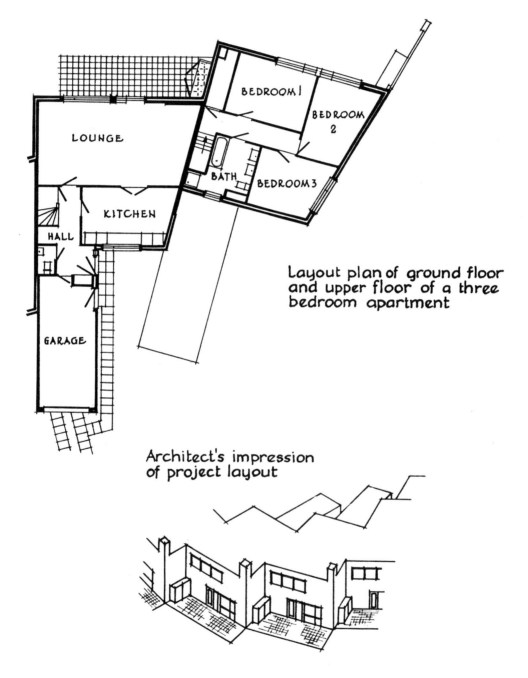

Layout plan of ground floor
and upper floor of a three
bedroom apartment

Architect's impression
of project layout

Figure 5.4

RELATIONSHIP BETWEEN PARTIES

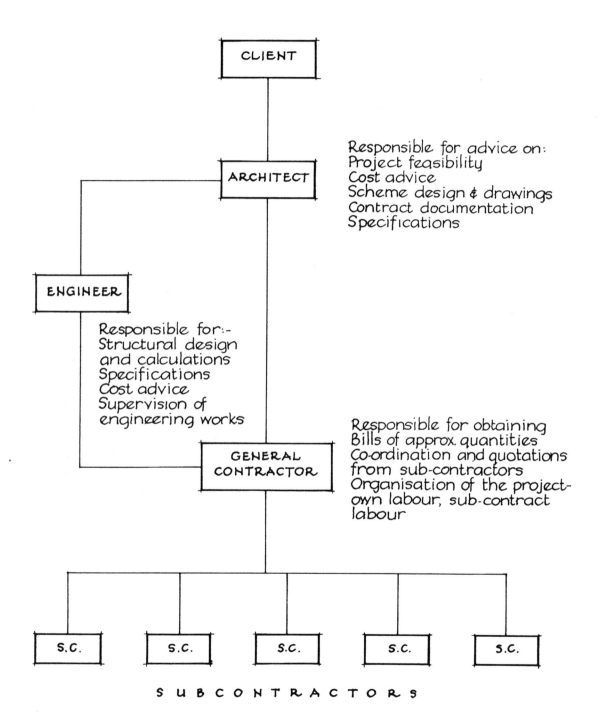

Figure 5.5

Architectural courses are currently being developed at polytechnics which combine full-time and part-time study programmes. These courses are of a less academic nature.

Level one involves four years of full-time study in relation to architecture design concepts and building techniques. On completion of level one the student obtains a position in an architectural practice.

A further four-year study programme is undertaken. This involves attending a academy of buildings for two and a half days per week with the remaining time being spent in the practice. On completion of the course programme the student qualifies as an architect.

The study programme covers a wide range of subject areas which include construction techniques, services and environmental studies. Emphasis is also placed upon aspects of architectural procedures, law and cost implications of architectural design.

The architect undertakes a major role in advising the client at the feasibility stage and his services incorporate the cost advice normally available from the quantity surveyor in the UK.

5.8 Role of the engineer

Engineers normally undertake a four year course at a university in order to obtain a diploma in engineering. Technical university courses are available at Delft, Eindhoven and Twente. The level of education is equivalent to a Masters degree and the engineer uses the designation IR.

The polytechnic institutions offer a bachelor degree with the designation ING. Engineering may be studied in a wide range of disciplines including technology, architectural design, housing and building management. Similar coursed are available in civil engineering with specialisms in traffic, hydraulics, construction and urban planning.

In principle the university trained engineers (IR), undertake practice as consultants, whilst the polytechnic trained engineer (ING) provides the technical back-up at both administrative and site level. The term engineer, therefore, covers a wide range of disciplines.

5.9 Role of the quantity surveyor

The quantity surveying function is undertaken by the architect as part of his professional service. No separate quantity surveying function exists, which is common with other countries in the EU.

The architect is responsible for providing cost advice at the project feasibility stage. The responsibility for assessing the quantities at the tender stage lies with the contractors who price the project. The contractor is responsible for preparing interim payment applications during the project.

The various polytechnic institutions throughout The Netherlands offer a four-year course of study leading to the award of a building engineer (ING) qualification). A range of building courses offers specialisms in:

Building technology
Building management
Housing renewal and social housing
Building techniques.

All the courses have a measurement and cost input and prepare students for work in the construction or local authority sector. The majority of building engineers undertake the role of 'technicians' in the construction industry and readily fill the gap between the craftsman and the university trained engineer.

5.10 Contractual arrangements and building procurement

Contractual procedures normally relate to standard contract clauses prescribed by government bodies. For small projects involving the construction of a small housing project of four to five house units the contractual arrangement as shown in section 5.6 will normally apply. The contractor is required to insure the building to cover defects liability for a period of 10 years after the contract completion.

Design and build contractual arrangements are not popular and are mainly applied to office development projects. The project management team approach is gaining popularity. This is similar in principle to the management contract arrangements used in the UK. It is common practice to appoint a main contractor to co-ordinate the various subcontract packages. Figure 5.6 illustrates the basic contractual arrangements for a major bank project.

5.11 Planning and building control procedures

Building control procedures are under the direct control of the local authority. Strict procedures are applicable to housing projects and the authority is responsible for checking and approving calculations submitted by professional engineers. Full calculations must be provided for foundations, suspended floors and stability of walls.

It is common practice for architects to submit standard construction details for local authority approval. Schematic dimensioned drawings then provide cross reference to the approved construction details. Building inspection is undertaken by a local authority inspector at excavation, foundation concreting and completion stage of a project.

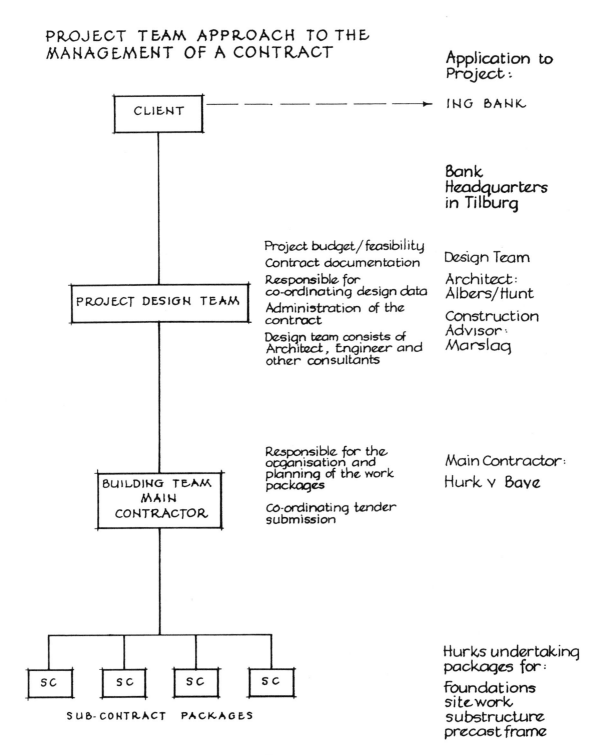

PROJECT TEAM APPROACH TO THE
MANAGEMENT OF A CONTRACT

Application to
Project:

CLIENT - - - - - - - - → ING BANK

Bank
Headquarters
in Tilburg

PROJECT DESIGN TEAM

Project budget / feasibility
Contract documentation
Responsible for
co-ordinating design data
Administration of the
contract
Design team consists of
Architect, Engineer and
other consultants

Design Team
Architect:
Albers/Hunt

Construction
Advisor:
Marslag

BUILDING TEAM
MAIN
CONTRACTOR

Responsible for the
organisation and
planning of the work
packages

Co-ordinating tender
submission

Main Contractor:
Hurk v Baye

SC SC SC SC

SUB-CONTRACT PACKAGES

Hurks undertaking
packages for:
foundations
site work
substructure
precast frame

Figure 5.6

5.12 Low rise housing construction

Information collection

The case study material outlined in the text relates to a number of housing projects in the Breda, Tilburg and Eindhoven areas of The Netherlands.

Data relating to the construction techniques has been obtained from current trade literature and during visits to social and residential housing developments. The construction techniques dealt with may not be typical of the building methods utilised in other parts of the country.

5.12.1 Form of construction

Low rise building techniques are mainly based on the cross-wall form of construction. At foundation level the crosswalls are carried on an arrangement of strip or piled foundations supporting precast concrete ground floor units.

The crosswalls may be formed of in situ concrete or precast walling blocks 100 mm in thickness. The crosswalls form the internal skin of the external wall construction together with the party or dividing wall between adjacent dwellings.

The first floor and floor at second floor ceiling level may be constructed of precast concrete wideslab units, or a precast plank floor may be used. The plank floor acts as a permanent soffit prior to the placing of the structural concrete topping. Temporary propping of the plank floors is necessary prior to concreting operations.

Externally, the house is clad in brickwork to the external elevations which incorporate the fixing of the cavity insulation and window and door frames.

In the majority of Dutch residential and social housing constructions the roof space is utilised as a habitable room. This may provide an additional bedroom, workshop or storage space area. Roof shapes are simply gabled with hips, and valleys are rarely used.

Maximum use is made of prefabricated modular components and the roof construction is no exception. Roof construction consists of a series of timber purlins spanning between the crosswalls. These support lightweight insulated deck slabs which span from eaves to ridge. The roof deck panels may incorporate roof lights or dormers. Roof finishes consist of concrete or clay tiles fixed to timber battens laid over the prefabricated roof decking panels.

Internal walls forming room separation may consist of storey height lightweight precast panels which are simply wedged between the ground floor and ceiling level. Internal wall surfaces are normally skimmed and painted. Ground and first floors are screeded, or a floating floor may be incorporated at first floor level.

In all Dutch housing construction the emphasis is on the use of prefabricated components and a reduction in the use of timber and wet trades.

Construction sequence study

Stage 1   *Construct internal crosswalls from foundation slab level to first floor. (Figure 5.9)*

For this purpose 100 mm thick interlocking precast concrete walling blocks are used. The blocks are 900 x 600 mm and, because of their weight, require moving into position with a small rubber-tyred mobile crane located on the foundation slab. Interlocking plastic cones are used in the horizontal wall joints to tie the blocks together. A grouted bed joint is laid between the walling units. Prior to erection of the walls, line profiles are set up at the corners of the building and at all internal wall junctions in order to ensure dimensional control, see fig 5.7.

Walling blocks are positioned to all building elevations incorporating openings for all door and window units.

Figure 5.7 also indicates the type of walling block used, figure 5.8 shows the plan layout of a linked housing unit. Load-bearing crosswalls are shown shaded on the diagram.

Stage 2   *Position precast concrete first floor units and provide propped support for precast concrete plank floors*

100 mm thick precast concrete wideslab floor units (1200 mm wide) are positioned, spanning between the internal crosswalls. Alternatively, precast concrete 60 mm thick plank floors may be used (1200 mm wide). The plank floor acts as permanent formwork prior to placing the in situ topping. Prior to concreting, the floor units require temporary propping at 1.5 m centres.

EXTERNAL WALL CONSTRUCTION

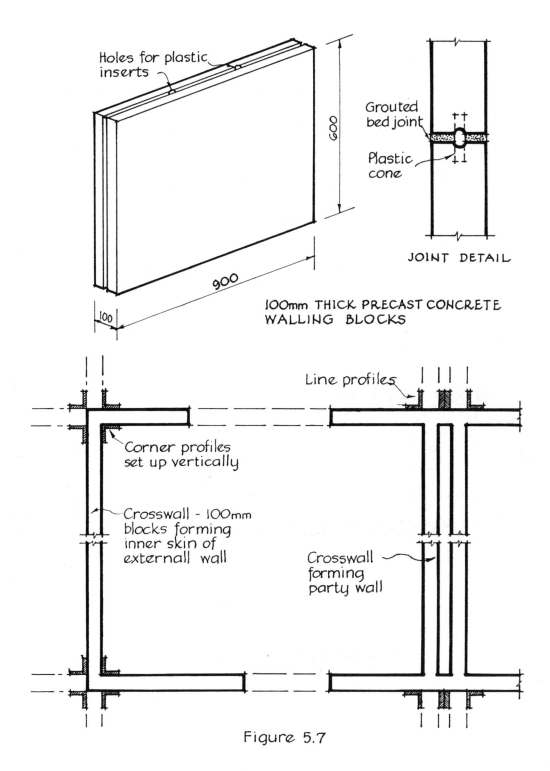

Holes for plastic inserts

600

900

100

100mm THICK PRECAST CONCRETE WALLING BLOCKS

Grouted bed joint

Plastic cone

JOINT DETAIL

Line profiles

Corner profiles set up vertically

Crosswall - 100mm blocks forming inner skin of externall wall

Crosswall forming party wall

Figure 5.7

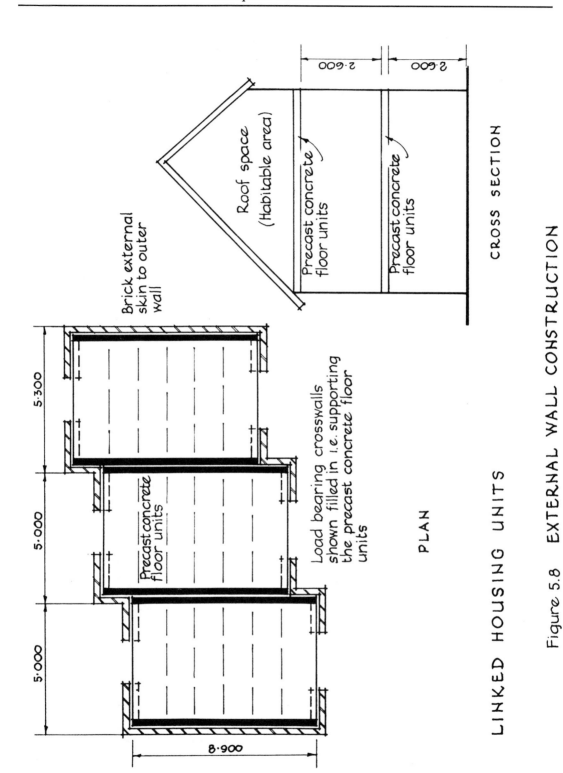

CROSS SECTION

Roof space
(Habitable area)

Precast concrete
floor units

Precast concrete
floor units

2·600

2·600

Brick external
skin to outer
wall

5·300

5·000

5·000

Precast concrete
floor units

Load bearing crosswalls
shown filled in i.e. supporting
the precast concrete floor
units

8·900

PLAN

LINKED HOUSING UNITS

Figure 5.8   EXTERNAL WALL CONSTRUCTION

Stage 3 Construct internal crosswalls from first floor level to second floor level (Figure 5.9)

Work proceeds with the erection of the precast concrete walling blocks to second floor level (ceiling level of the first floor).

As an alternative to using precast concrete walling blocks, in situ concrete walls may be constructed using floor to ceiling height formwork.

Stage 4 Erect precast concrete floor at second floor level (Figure 5.10)

Construct second floor using precast concrete units as for stage 2. Use temporary props as necessary and place structural concrete topping.

Stage 5 Construct gable crosswalls to roof line (Figure 5.10)

Construct internal crosswall to roof gables, to follow line of roof profile, using precast walling blocks as before.

Stage 6 Construct external face of walls using brickwork (Figure 5.10)

Construct external wall to perimeter of building. This will involve first fixing cavity insulation to the outer face of the inner wall. This is secured in position with patent ties. Form a 25 mm cavity and construct the brick external wall to incorporate all external window and door frames.

During the construction of the external walls work will normally proceed with the construction of the timber purlins and decking slabs to the roof.

Figure 5.11 illustrates a diagrammatic view of the wall and floor construction showing the sequence of work using precast concrete walling blocks and plank floor units. Figure 5.12 illustrates the arrangement of the crosswalls and floors using in situ concrete construction. Figure 5.13 indicates the use of precast units for the main floor components.

5.13 Case study – low rise housing construction

5.13.1 Case study – three linked housing units

Section 5.13.8 describes a case study relating to a low rise housing development at Reeshof in the Tilbury area.

CONSTRUCTION SEQUENCE STUDY

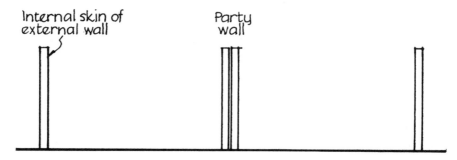

Internal skin of external wall

Party wall

STAGE 1

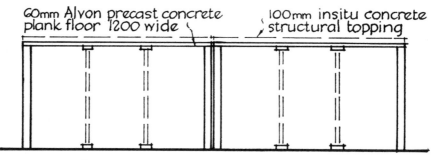

60mm Alvon precast concrete plank floor 1200 wide

100mm insitu concrete structural topping

STAGE 2

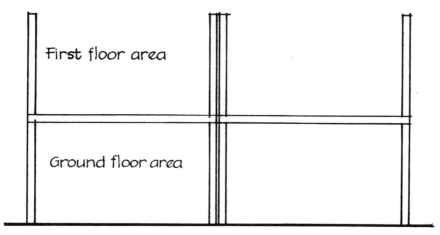

First floor area

Ground floor area

STAGE 3

SEQUENCE OF CONSTRUCTION

Figure 5.9

CONSTRUCTION SEQUENCE STUDY

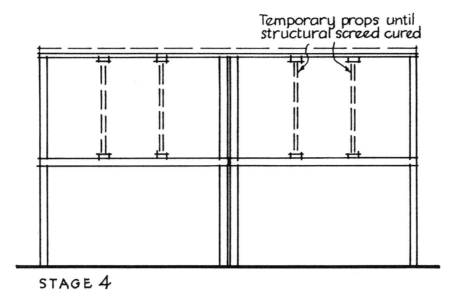

Temporary props until
structural screed cured

STAGE 4

On completion of the
gable wall, external
brickwork constructed

Roof space area

1st floor area

Ground floor area

STAGES 5 AND 6

SEQUENCE OF CONSTRUCTION

Figure 5.10

CONSTRUCTION SEQUENCE STUDY

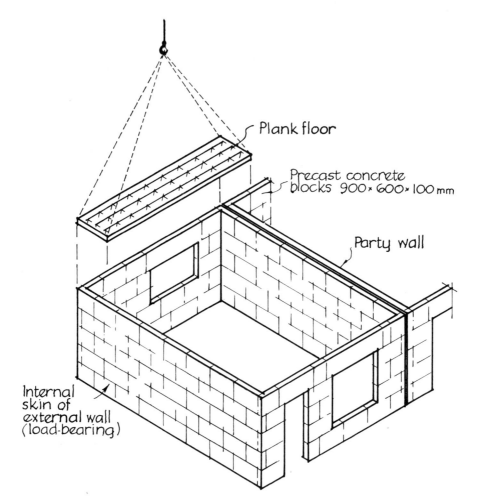

Plank floor

Precast concrete blocks 900 × 600 × 100 mm

Party wall

Internal skin of external wall (load-bearing)

SPAN OF FLOOR

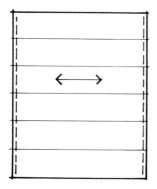

CROSSWALL CONSTRUCTION USING PRECAST CONCRETE WALLING BLOCKS

Figure 5.11

CONSTRUCTION SEQUENCE STUDY

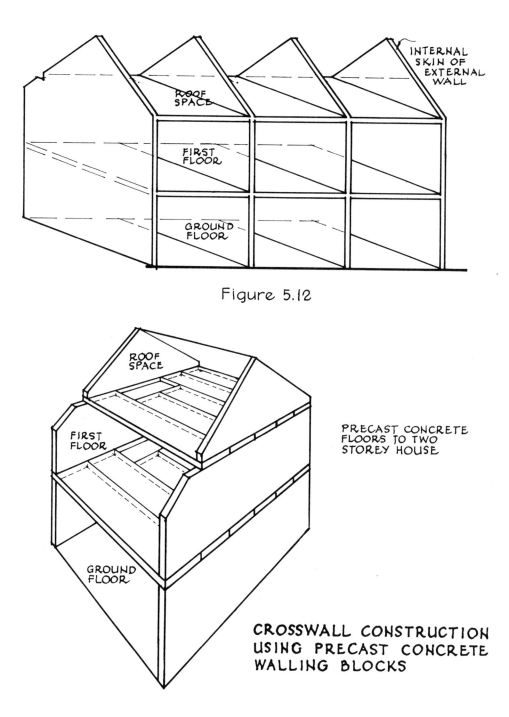

INTERNAL SKIN OF EXTERNAL WALL

ROOF SPACE

FIRST FLOOR

GROUND FLOOR

Figure 5.12

ROOF SPACE

FIRST FLOOR

GROUND FLOOR

PRECAST CONCRETE FLOORS TO TWO STOREY HOUSE

CROSSWALL CONSTRUCTION USING PRECAST CONCRETE WALLING BLOCKS

Figure 5.13

The 56-unit development is planned around linked blocks of four and six units laid out in two quadrangles. The site plan is shown in figure 5.31.

The case study relates to a block of three linked house units commonly found on development sites in The Netherlands. The elements of construction to be dealt with include foundations, ground floor, external walls, floor and roof details.

5.13.2 Foundation element

Figure 5.14 indicates a foundation plan of the three house units together with a sketch cross section through the strip foundation, in situ ground beams and precast ground floor slab.

Strip foundation widths vary from 900 mm on the front and rear walls to 1200 mm on the crosswalls. It is common practice to excavate oversite to the underside of the strip foundation level prior to constructing the reinforced strip and ground beam foundation. Ground beams may be constructed of in situ concrete or built in cavity brickwork or blockwork.

Figure 5.15 illustrates a section through a strip and beam foundation overlying a firm sand strata, whilst figure 5.16 illustrates an in situ concrete ground beam supported on piles.

In the majority of situations a void is incorporated under the ground floor in order to accommodate services. Extensive use is made of district heating systems which bring heating service pipes into each dwelling. Ventilation under the floor is provided by means of patent plastic ventilation ducts located around the perimeter of the foundation.

Figure 5.17 illustrates the use of brickwork and blockwork walls to support the ground floor slab.

5.13.3 Ground floor element

Suspended precast concrete floor are used to form the ground floor slab. The precast concrete floor incorporates a layer of 40-60 mm polystyrene insulation foam cast on the underside of the units at the manufacturing stage.

A large variety of precast floor types are available varying in thickness from 180 mm to 300 mm. The floor units span between the crosswall ground beams. Figure 5.18, details A to C, illustrate a range of floor systems available to both the designer and contractor.

FOUNDATION CONSTRUCTION

LINKED HOUSING UNITS

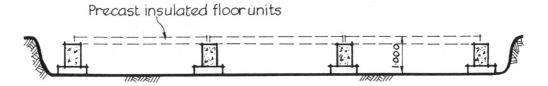

Extent of
stip foundations

1200 mm wide

Precast
concrete
floors

1200mm wide

900mm wide

5·700

5·000

900mm wide

900mm wide PLAN

X — X

Precast insulated floor units

1·000

SECTION X-X

IN SITU CONCRETE GROUND BEAMS
ON STRIP FOUNDATIONS

Figure 5.14

FOUNDATION CONSTRUCTION

FOUNDATION DETAILS

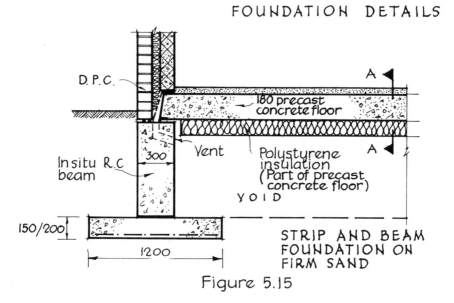

D.P.C.

180 precast concrete floor

In situ R.C beam

300

Vent

Polystyrene insulation (Part of precast concrete floor)

VOID

150/200

1200

STRIP AND BEAM FOUNDATION ON FIRM SAND

A

A

Figure 5.15

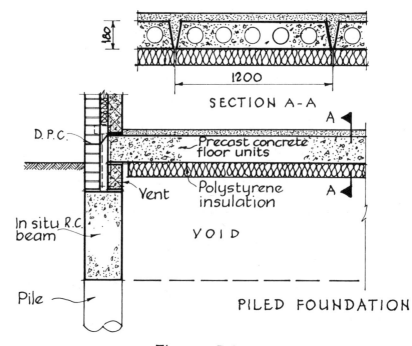

180

1200

SECTION A-A

D.P.C.

Precast concrete floor units

Polystyrene insulation

In situ R.C. beam

Vent

VOID

Pile

PILED FOUNDATION

A

A

Figure 5.16

FOUNDATION CONSTRUCTION

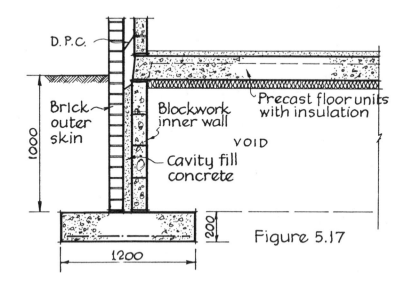

D.P.C.

Brick outer skin

Blockwork inner wall

Cavity fill concrete

Precast floor units with insulation

VOID

1000

200

1200

Figure 5.17

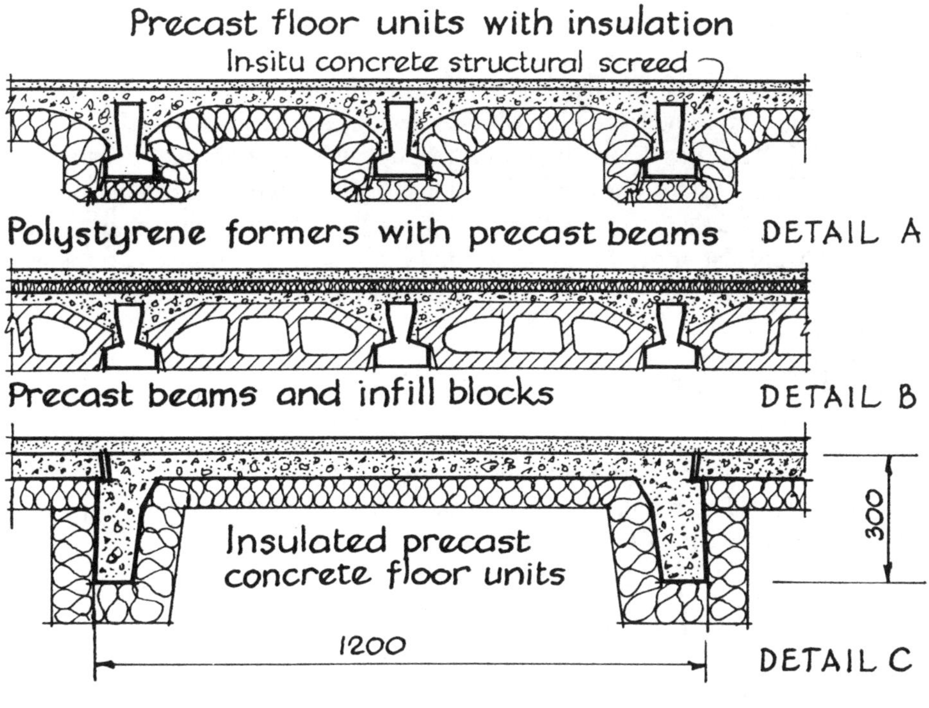

Precast floor units with insulation

In-situ concrete structural screed

Polystyrene formers with precast beams   DETAIL A

Precast beams and infill blocks   DETAIL B

Insulated precast concrete floor units

300

1200   DETAIL C

Figure 5.18

Precast floor type A consists of polystyrene interlocking formers placed between precast concrete I beams. An in situ concrete structural screed is laid over the formers to form the structural floor.

Precast floor type B consists of a beam and concrete block floor similar to those used in the UK and France.

Precast floor type C consists of 1200 mm wide trough units preformed on 100 mm thick insulated formers. The trough units are factory made, delivered to site and positioned by crane between the foundation crosswalls as shown in figure 5.19.

Figure 5.20 illustrates the layout of the precast units to the ground floor area. Detailed sections indicate the construction of a solid ground floor laid on a compacted formation. It is common practice to use solid ground floors for the garage units, which are often located between the linked blocks of houses.

5.13.4 External wall elements

The sequence of constructing the external wall elements using precast concrete interlocking blocks or in situ concrete was previously outlined in the stages 1 to 6 in section 5.12.

Figure 5.21 illustrates alternative details of the external wall construction. The internal skin of the external wall is erected without the aid of an external scaffold as the blocks are positioned by working off the floors of the building. On completion of the internal wall and gables, work commences simultaneously on the roof and external wall construction. An external scaffold is erected prior to fixing the cavity insulation and the external wall facings, so some consideration appears to be given towards the aspects of construction safety.

Figure 5.22 indicates detailed sections through the external wall at ground floor, window sill and lintel level showing the positioning of the insulation.

Figure 5.23 illustrates a sketch section through the external wall construction for the linked housing units. This shows the relationships between the crosswalls and the floor construction. A detailed section through the crosswall is illustrated in figure 5.24 highlighting details at roof, first and ground floor levels. This shows the relationship between the floor and the wall connections and fixing of the timber purlins at roof level.

5.13.5 Thermal requirements

The thermal insulation requirements are shown in figure 5.25 for walls, roof and ground floor construction. The requirements are based on an internal temperture of 22°C and an external temperature of 10°C to −5°C.

FOUNDATION CONSTRUCTION

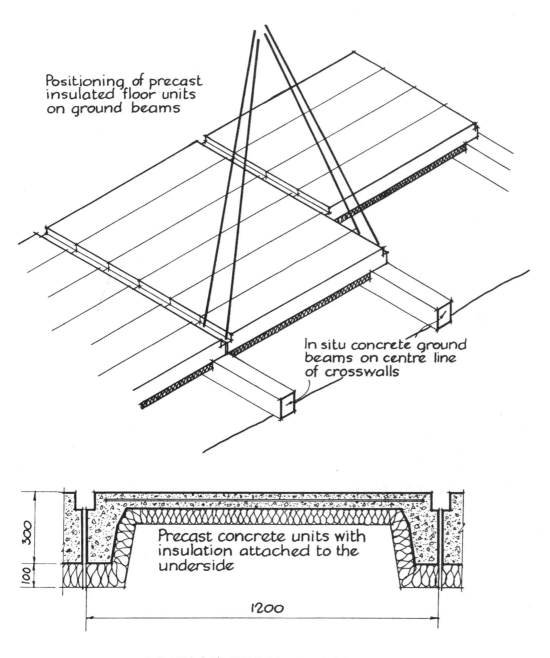

Positioning of precast
insulated floor units
on ground beams

In situ concrete ground
beams on centre line
of crosswalls

300
100
1200

Precast concrete units with
insulation attached to the
underside

SECTION THROUGH PRECAST
FLOOR UNITS

Figure 5.19

FOUNDATION CONSTRUCTION

LAYOUT OF GROUND FLOOR

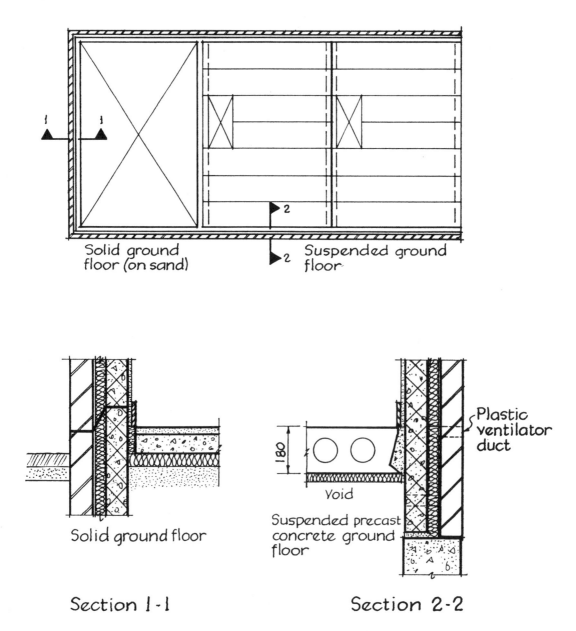

Solid ground floor (on sand)

Suspended ground floor

Solid ground floor

Section 1-1

Suspended precast concrete ground floor

Void

180

Plastic ventilator duct

Section 2-2

Figure 5.20

EXTERNAL WALL CONSTRUCTION

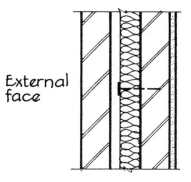

External
face

100 mm brick external facing
100 mm cavity - 20 mm airspace
                    80 mm insulation
100 mm internal brick or blockwork
 10 mm plaster skim finish

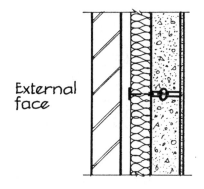

External
face

100 mm brick external facing
100 mm cavity as above
100 mm precast blocks
  5 mm plaster skim finish

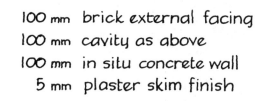

External
face

100 mm brick external facing
100 mm cavity as above
100 mm in situ concrete wall
  5 mm plaster skim finish

ALTERNATIVE EXTERNAL WALL CONSTRUCTION

Figure 5.21

EXTERNAL WALL CONSTRUCTION

TYPICAL EXTERNAL WALL DETAILS

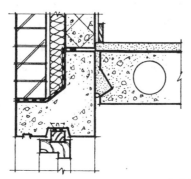
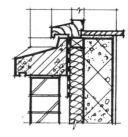

LINTELS

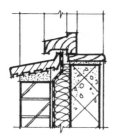

SILLS

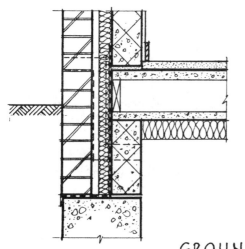

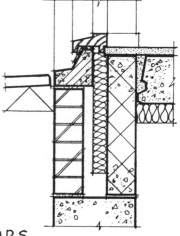

GROUND FLOORS

Figure 5.22

EXTERNAL WALL CONSTRUCTION

ELEMENT - EXTERNAL WALLS AND FLOORS

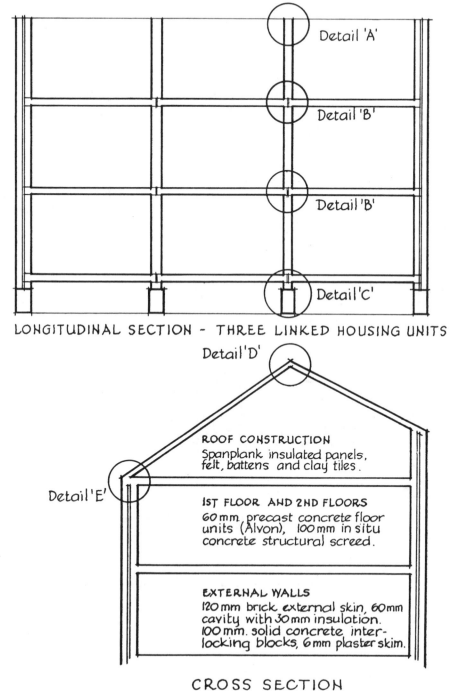

Detail 'A'

Detail 'B'

Detail 'B'

Detail 'C'

LONGITUDINAL SECTION - THREE LINKED HOUSING UNITS

Detail 'D'

Detail 'E'

ROOF CONSTRUCTION
Spanplank insulated panels, felt, battens and clay tiles.

1ST FLOOR AND 2ND FLOORS
60mm. precast concrete floor units (Alvon), 100mm in situ concrete structural screed.

EXTERNAL WALLS
120mm brick external skin, 60mm cavity with 30mm insulation. 100mm. solid concrete interlocking blocks, 6mm plaster skim.

CROSS SECTION

Figure 5.23

EXTERNAL WALL CONSTRUCTION

DETAIL A

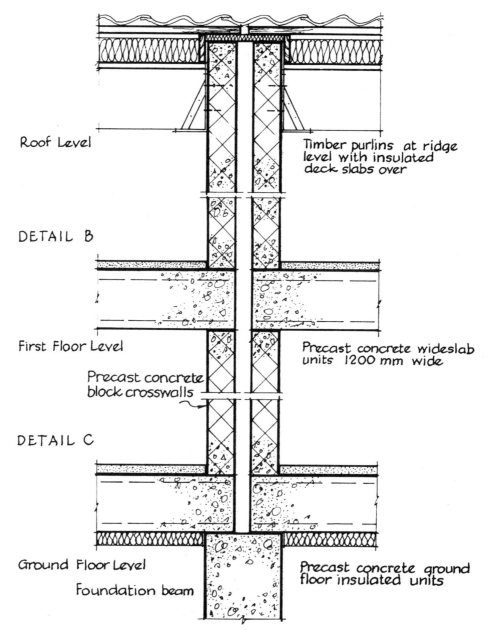

Roof Level

Timber purlins at ridge
level with insulated
deck slabs over

DETAIL B

First Floor Level

Precast concrete wideslab
units 1200 mm wide

Precast concrete
block crosswalls

DETAIL C

Ground Floor Level

Foundation beam

Precast concrete ground
floor insulated units

Figure 5.24

THERMAL INSULATION REQUIREMENTS ('U' VALUES)

Temperature Ranges
  Internal temperature - 22°C
  External temperature - 10° to -5°C

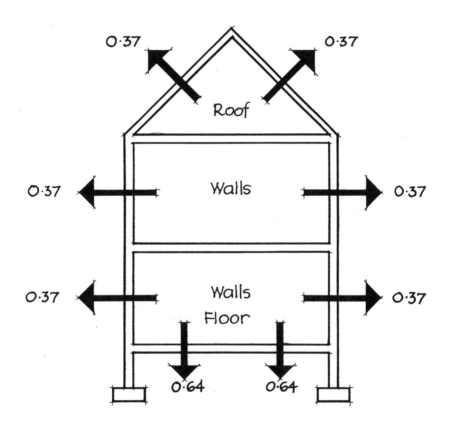

Dutch Code for thermal insulation values - N.E.N 1068

Figure 5.25

5.13.6 Suspended floor element

Suspended floors at first floor and first floor ceiling level are formed of precast concrete units spanning between the crosswalls. The type of floor specified may be of the following three types:

i)   Precast concrete wideslab floors
ii)   Precast plank floors
iii)   Beam and block floors.

Precast concrete wideslab units are up to 1200 mm in width and form an instant working platform.

Plank floor consist of 60 mm thick precast units laid to form a permanent soffit. The 1200 mm wide units require temporary propping prior to placing the 100 mm thick structural slab. The system of plank floors is widely used in other European countries where the planks may be prefabricated on site (see the French case study in section 3.15).

On smaller, one-off housing projects, prestressed beam and infill blocks may be specified. This system has the advantage that it does not require a crane to position the light prestressed floor units.

5.13.7 Roof element

The construction of the roof element in The Netherlands is considered most innovative. The roof construction is based on fixing timber or precast concrete purlins between the crosswalls and covering them with insulated roof panels which are then tiled. This method eliminates the use of timber roof trusses and enables the roof space to be fully used as a habitable room or storage area. Figure 5.26 illustrates the sequence of constructing the roof.

Figure 5.27 illustrates the method of securing the purlins at eaves level to the concrete floor slab using metal straps. The insulated roof panels are simply nailed to the timber purlins. Figure 5.28 indicates details of the construction of the roof deck panels which are available in widths form 610 mm to 1220 mm. Owing to the lightness of the deck panels these may be manhandled into position.

Figure 5.29, details D and E indicate ridge and eaves details showing a variety of fixing details.

On completion of the positioning of the deck slabs, the roof is battened and tiles to give the appearance of a traditional roof. On long span roofs, insulated deck slabs may be delivered in large panels and handled by cranes.

ROOF CONSTRUCTION

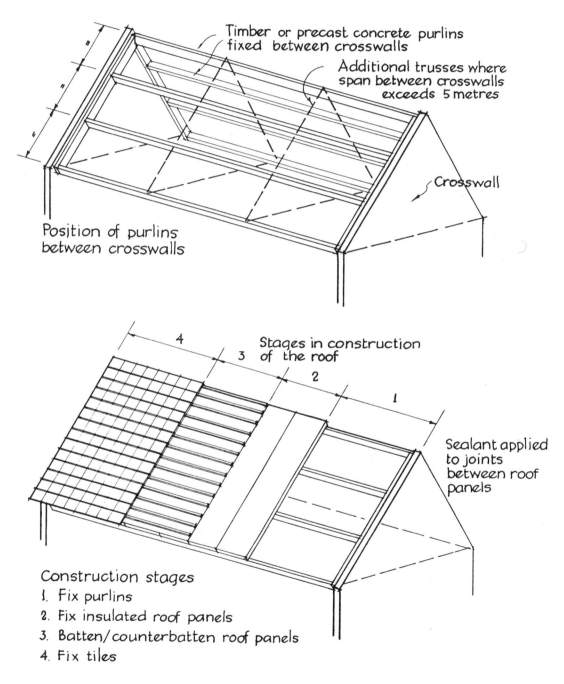

Timber or precast concrete purlins fixed between crosswalls

Additional trusses where span between crosswalls exceeds 5 metres

Crosswall

Position of purlins between crosswalls

Stages in construction of the roof

Sealant applied to joints between roof panels

Construction stages
1. Fix purlins
2. Fix insulated roof panels
3. Batten/counterbatten roof panels
4. Fix tiles

Figure 5.26

ROOF CONSTRUCTION

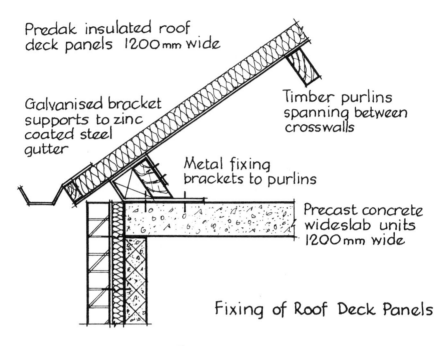

Predak insulated roof deck panels 1200 mm wide

Galvanised bracket supports to zinc coated steel gutter

Timber purlins spanning between crosswalls

Metal fixing brackets to purlins

Precast concrete wideslab units 1200 mm wide

Fixing of Roof Deck Panels

Figure 5.27

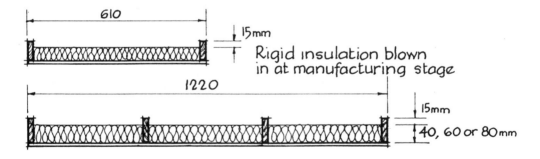

610

15mm

Rigid insulation blown in at manufacturing stage

1220

15mm

40, 60 or 80mm

Insulated Roof Deck Panels

Spanplank, Cenkospan, Predak, Opstalan or similar, 9mm-16mm plywood base, 20mm x 80mm softwood timber at 400-600mm centres, 40, 60 or 80mm polystyrene insulation blown in at the manufacturing stage.

Figure 5.28

ROOF CONSTRUCTION

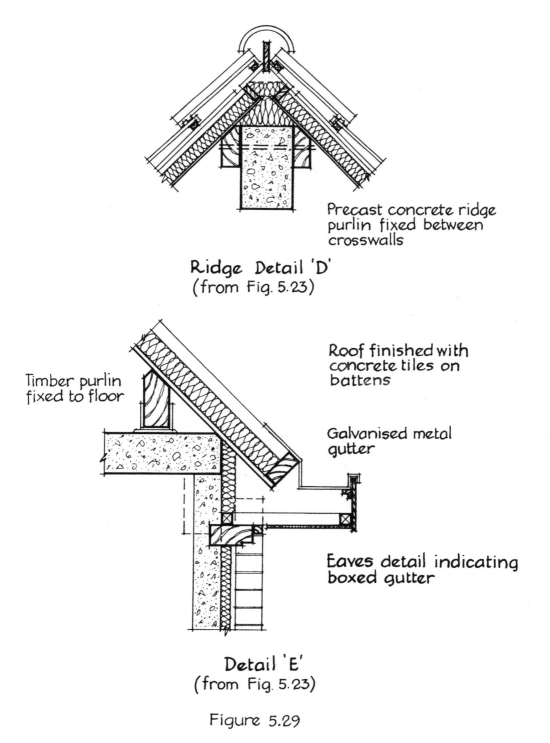

Precast concrete ridge purlin fixed between crosswalls

Ridge Detail 'D'
(from Fig. 5.23)

Roof finished with concrete tiles on battens

Timber purlin fixed to floor

Galvanised metal gutter

Eaves detail indicating boxed gutter

Detail 'E'
(from Fig. 5.23)

Figure 5.29

ROOF CONSTRUCTION

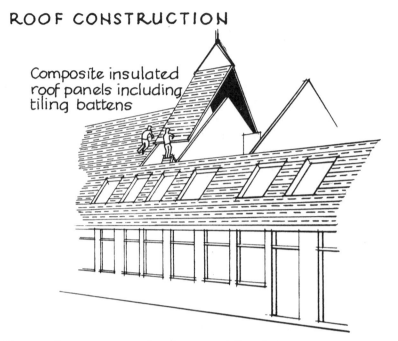

Composite insulated
roof panels including
tiling battens

Hinged roof panels being lifted into position

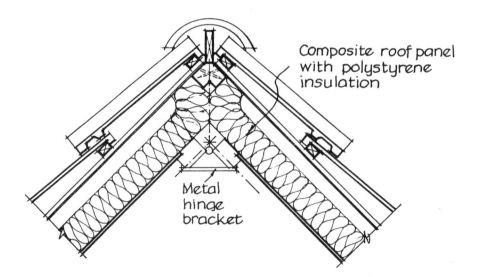

Composite roof panel
with polystyrene
insulation

Metal
hinge
bracket

Ridge detail of hinged joint

Figure 5.30

The panels may incorporate rooflights within the sloping areas. Other innovations include the use of hinged roof sections as illustrated in figure 5.30. Observations indicated a considerable reduction in the number of manhours to complete the carcassing and covering to the Dutch style roof. The reduction in the amount of timber used in the construction aids the environmental problems and results in cost savings and a better insulated roof.

Perhaps some UK contractors will consider this form of construction as a viable alternative to the trussed roof construction currently used in the UK.

5.13.8 Case study – Social housing development – Reeshof – Tilburg

Project details

The Reeshof development in Tilburg (Brabant) forms one of the largest social and residential developments in the south of The Netherlands. Up to 5000 low rise housing units have been built to form the Reeshof district to the east of Tilburg.

Figure 5.31 illustrates a site layout plan for a phase containing 56 terraced units to be constructed in fourteen blocks. In this way the project may be readily divided into contracts capable of being undertaken by local, medium sized housing contractors.

Figure 5.32 contains an architect's impression of a completed block of four terraced housing units. Floor plans and a typical building cross section and plan of the roof are shown in figure 5.33, and for the house type A.

Building techniques

Foundation works consist of in situ concrete, wide strip foundations supporting brick walls carrying an arrangement of insulated precast concrete floor units.

The crosswall construction utilises precast concrete walling blocks supporting precast concrete floor units at first floor level.

Externally, the houses are faced in concrete bricks manufactured using a silica aggregate which enables a stonework appearance to be achieved.

Roof construction consists of timber purlins supporting pre-formed insulated roof panels 1200 mm wide. The roof panels are spiked to the purlins and secured to the edge of the precast floor units at the eaves level. Galvanised metal rainwater gutters are incorporated at the eaves.

Internal walls may be constructed of smooth faced concrete blocks (300 × 225 mm high) and 75 or 100 mm thick. Alternatively, 600 mm wide lightweight concrete, storey-height panels may be used for internal partitions.

CASE STUDY - REESHOF DEVELOPMENT - TILBURG

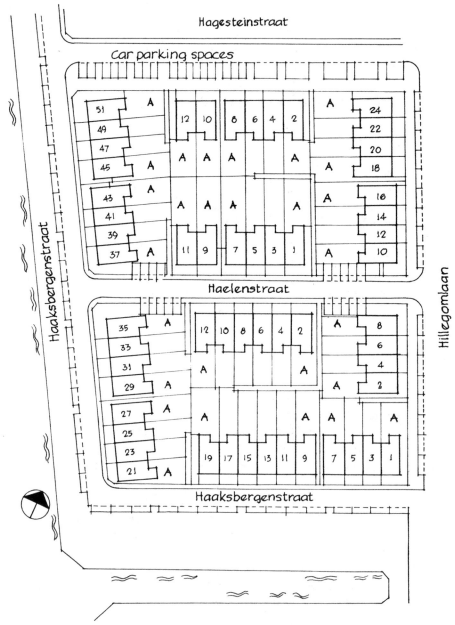

SITE PLAN

Figure 5.31

CASE STUDY - REESHOF DEVELOPMENT -TILBURG

Architects perspective of
low rise housing units

Figure 5.32

CASE STUDY - REESHOF DEVELOPMENT - TILBURG

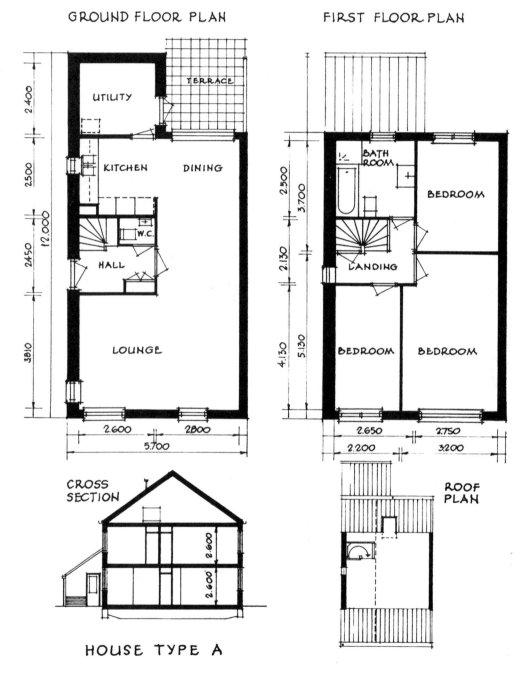

GROUND FLOOR PLAN

FIRST FLOOR PLAN

CROSS SECTION

ROOF PLAN

HOUSE TYPE A

Figure 5.33

Joints between the vertical panels are scrim-jointed prior to applying a 2 mm plaster skim coat. The soffits of the precast concrete floors are spray painted in order to achieve a textured paint finish.

Ground and suspended floors are screeded to receive tiles or carpets. Electrical services are incorporated in the floor screeds, together with hot and cold water pipes. Service drops to lighting points in ceilings are incorporated in the precast concrete floor units.

All internal wall surfaces are skim plaster-coated direct to the smooth concrete walling blocks prior to wallpapering or painting.

Traditional timber or PVCu window and door frames may be incorporated with double glazed units. Heating services are provided by a site-based district heating plant which utilises waste heat produced by adjacent industrial developments.

Site landscaping features incorporate canals which are linked into the regional canal network. These form an important feature of the site and may include timber access bridges and recreational areas.

Housing styles are somewhat unimaginative but functional. They are designed within strict cost limits to meet the need of a large social housing programme.

5.14 Medium rise construction

Information collection

The case study material outlined in the text relates to the Badhotel project at Domburg in the Walcheren region. The complex consists of a 114 apartment hotel and five three-storey blocks of flats.

Form of construction

Medium rise buildings are taken to be structures between three and ten storeys in height. Forms of construction used for buildings based on a repetition plan layout on each floor are normally constructed of crosswall construction. This form of construction is suitable for the frame element of residential flats, social housing projects and hotel complexes. Figure 5.34 illustrates the application of crosswall construction to a hotel project in Hoorn.

Crosswall construction incorporates in situ concrete walls at 3.8 to 5.5 metre centres supporting in situ or precast floor components. Plank floors may be introduced to act as permanent formwork prior to placing the structural floor.

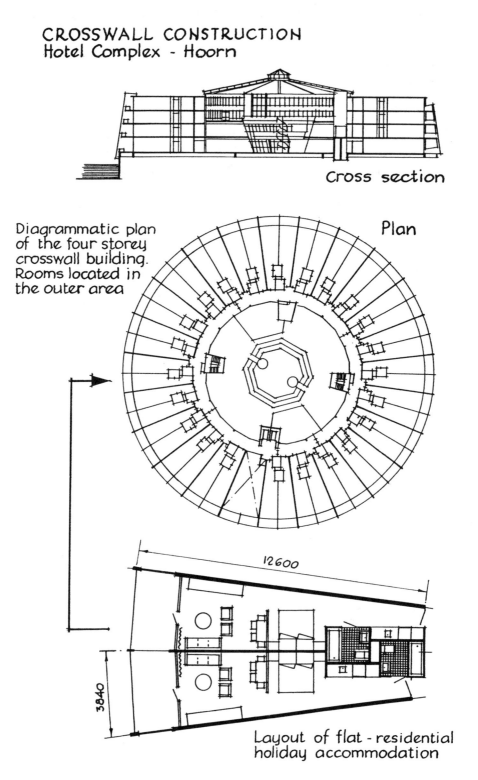

CROSSWALL CONSTRUCTION
Hotel Complex - Hoorn

Cross section

Diagrammatic plan
of the four storey
crosswall building.
Rooms located in
the outer area

Plan

12600

3840

Layout of flat - residential
holiday accommodation

Figure 5.34

HURKS PRECAST FRAME SYSTEM

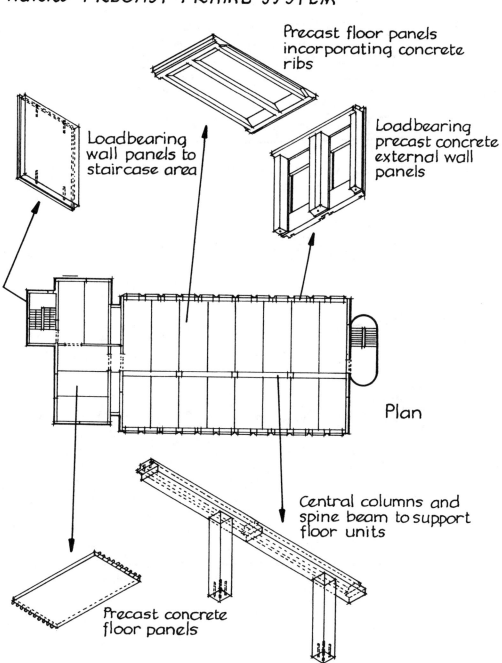

Precast floor panels incorporating concrete ribs

Loadbearing wall panels to staircase area

Loadbearing precast concrete external wall panels

Plan

Central columns and spine beam to support floor units

Precast concrete floor panels

Load-bearing wall and central spine arrangement

Figure 5.35

DOUBLE T PRECAST FRAME SYSTEM

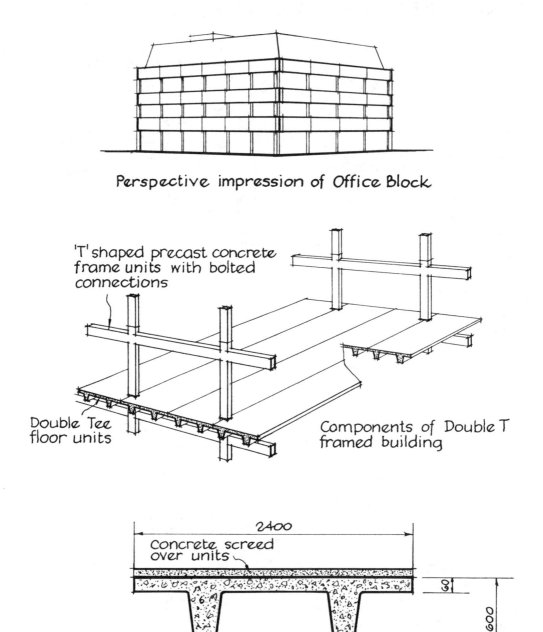

Perspective impression of Office Block

'T' shaped precast concrete frame units with bolted connections

Double Tee floor units

Components of Double T framed building

2400

Concrete screed over units

600

150

Double T floor component

Figure 5.36

Extensive use is made of patent formwork systems for the wall and floor pours. The use of tunnel shutters is a common feature in The Netherlands as this technique improves the cycle time per floor. Cycle times of 1 to 3 weeks per floor can be achieved depending upon the building plan size, shape and complexity. Staircases may be located centrally or at the end of blocks to aid the means of access and escape. Crosswall construction relies structurally on obtaining continuity at wall and floor joints. Extensive use is made of mobile and tower cranes for handling of wall shutters, table forms, reinforcement and precast floor units. Concrete pumping is the norm for both wall and floor pours.

Precast frame construction

Alternative forms of medium rise construction are based on the use of precast concrete frames. Frame systems vary from the standard frame of columns, beams and wideslab floor units through to the loadbearing wall frame systems. Figure 5.35 illustrates a frame system developed by Hurks, which incorporates a cental spine of columns and beams to support the trough type floor units. Other systems developed include the TT frame which is illustrated in figure 5.36. A range of precast systems have been developed by contractors offering a complete design, manufacture and erect package.

5.15 Case study – medium rise construction

The Badhotel project – Domburg – Zeeland

Figure 5.37 indicates a site location plan of the hotel and flats complex. A part front elevation of the four storey hotel building is shown in figure 5.38 together with an elevation of the crosswall layout behind the facade. The 200 mm thick in situ crosswalls to the uppers floors are located at 3.8 metre centre. The first floor slab is supported on a series of columns located under the crosswalls in order to provide an open plan area to the ground floor as shown in figure 5.39. The foundations are supported on a series of precast concrete piles connected by ground beams. Figure 5.40 illustrates a layout of part of the foundations together with sections through the supporting ground beams and suspended ground floor slab which is constructed using 60 mm thick precast plank floor slabs as shown in figure 5.41. The void formed under the ground floor slab is used to accommodate building services.

Construction techniques for the in situ crosswalls at 1st, 2nd and 3rd floor levels are similar to those used in France (see section 3.15).

THE BADHOTEL PROJECT - DOMBURG - ZEELAND

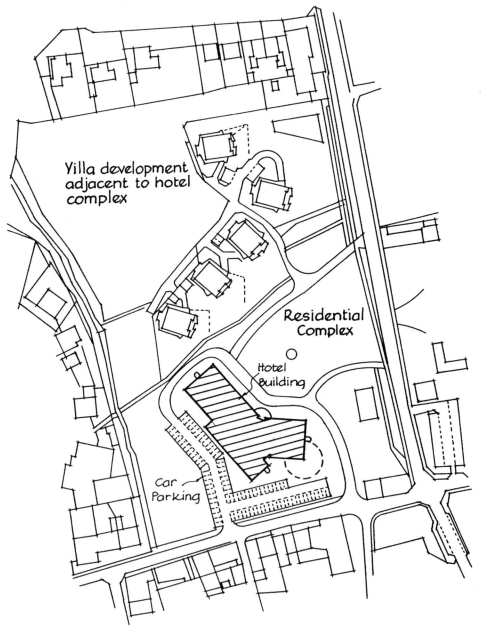

Location Plan

Figure 5.37

THE BADHOTEL PROJECT - DOMBURG - ZEELAND

Part Front Elevation
4 Storey Residential Complex

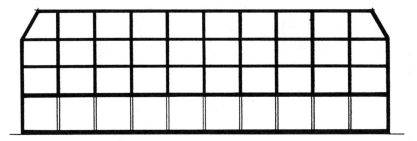

Exposed view of crosswall frame

Crosswalls at 3·8 metre centres supported on
columns at ground floor level.   Crosswall
construction to 1st, 2nd and 3rd floors

Figure 5.38

THE BADHOTEL PROJECT - DOMBURG - ZEELAND

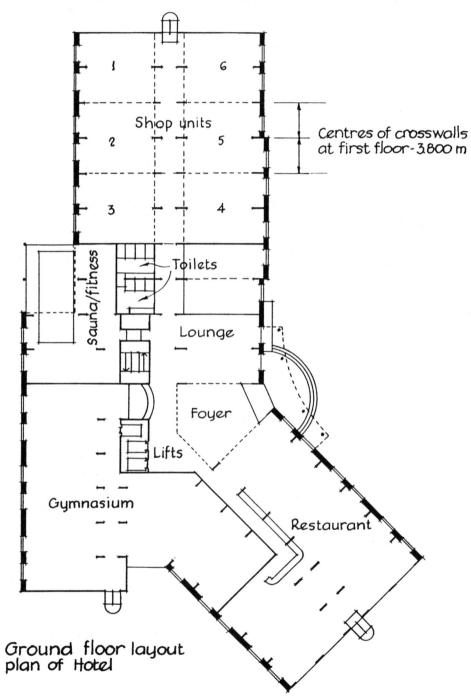

Ground floor layout plan of Hotel

Figure 5.39.

THE BADHOTEL PROJECT - DOMBURG - ZEELAND

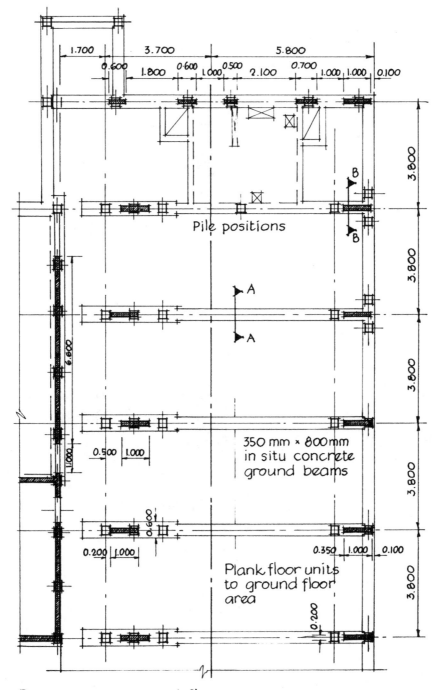

Part plan of ground floor

Figure 5.40

THE BADHOTEL PROJECT - DOMBURG - ZEELAND

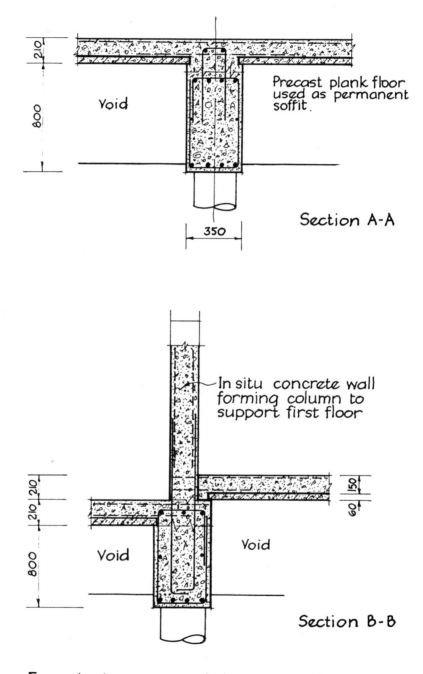

Void

Precast plank floor
used as permanent
soffit.

Section A-A

In situ concrete wall
forming column to
support first floor

Void

Void

Section B-B

Foundation ground beam sections

Figure 5.41

THE BADHOTEL PROJECT – DOMBURG – ZEELAND

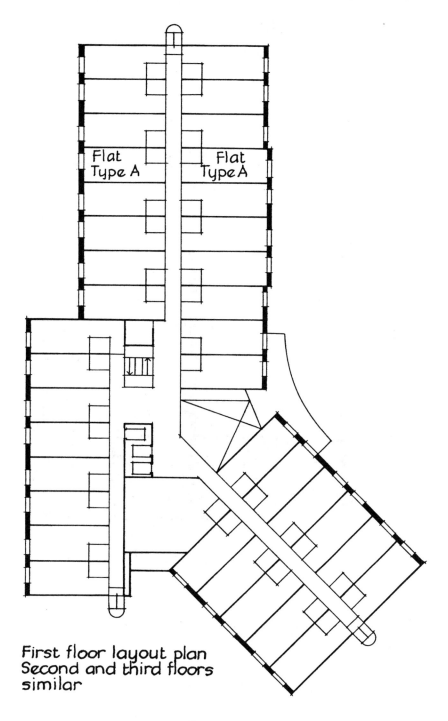

Flat Type A

Flat Type A

First floor layout plan
Second and third floors
similar

Figure 5.42

THE BADHOTEL PROJECT – DOMBURG – ZEELAND

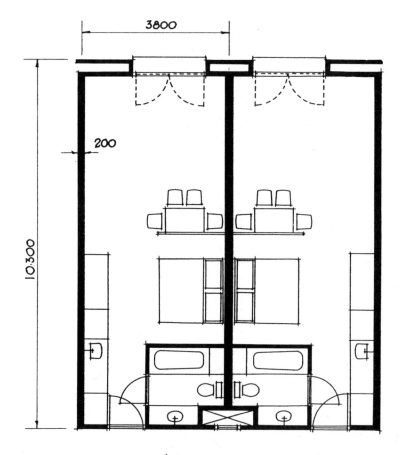

Detailed Layout Plan
Flat Type A
One Bedroom Apartment

Figure 5.43

The 200 mm thick crosswalls are cast using patent storey height formwork. Precast plank floors are again incorporated for the suspended floor slab construction. The use of plank floors eliminates the need for using soffit formwork and speeds up the construction process.

Figure 5.42 illustrates the floor layout plan at first, second and third floor levels showing the crosswall layout. Repetitive construction of this type is economical in the use of both plant and formwork. Figure 5.43 illustrates an internal layout plan of a one bedroomed apartment providing an internal floor area of approximately 37 square metres.

Externally the in situ concrete envelope is insulated with 60 mm fibreglass and brickwork applied to the elevations. External features are enhanced by the attractive treatment of external windows and the introduction of timber shutters to the ground floor windows.

Apartment and flat prices

The sale price of a one-bedroomed apartment within the hotel complex ranges from 150 000 to 200 000 Dfl. per unit (£54 500-£127 270). The two-bedroomed luxury flats with the villa complex are priced in the 280 000 to 350 000 Dfl. range (£101 800-£127 200). This attractive development is close to the beach and provides an ideal summer retreat in superb surroundings in the province of Zeeland.

6 The Construction Industry in Portugal

6.1 Key information

Capital – Lisbon
Area (sq. km) 91 985   Population 9.86m (1991)

6.2 Construction output

Output data for 1986 is shown in millions of pounds based on an exchange rate of 200 escudos to the pound.

Year	Building	Public Works	Maintenance
1986	3900	1800	620

Construction output in 1986 was approximately some £6.3 billion with new building work accounting for 60% of the total output.

The general quality of building work is variable. Buildings standards in the up-market commercial developments in Lisbon are good. As in other countries, quality standards tend to fall during periods of 'rapid expansion'. Standards of construction are low on the speculative flats and villa developments on the Algarve.

In 1990 the government considered placing a one year embargo on villa developments in certain regions of the Algarve, as they considered that building in the tourist ares had become somewhat out of control.

Building prices – labour and materials

Key labour rates for labourers and craftsmen engaged in the construction industry are shown. The range of key material prices are indicated in order that comparisons may be made between each country.

Labour rate	Basic rate (per hour)	All-in-rate (per hour)
Unskilled labour	£1.18 (260 esc)	£2.32 (515 esc)
Craftsmen	£1.45 (320 esc)	£2.92 (645 esc)

The rate per day for labour only gangs engaged in developments in the Algarve are as follows:

Unskilled labour	£8-10 per day
Skilled bricklayer	£10-14 per day
Skilled plasterers	£12-16 per day

	Unit	Price	
Material rates		esc	£
High yield steel	tonne	85 000	384
Structural steel	tonne	93 000	418
Ordinary cement	tonne	13 000	58
Carcasing timber	Cubic metre	84 000	380
Clay bricks	1000	50 000	226
Concrete blocks	Square metre	928	4.2
Apartments – cost per square metre	Range low	80 000	365
	high	97 000	442
Factory units–cost per square metre	Range low	41 000	185
	high	71 000	321

Value Added Tax (1993)   General level 25% Applicable to building

Data obtained from *Building* – 22 January 1993 – Procurement – European Costings

6.3 Review of the construction industry

The construction industry consists mainly of large numbers of small and medium sized family enterprises. Over 80% of the 28 000 building contractors employ less than ten workers. A predominantly large sub-contract market is in evidence in the villa developments in the coastal areas of the Algarve.

Less than 3% of all enterprises employ more than fifty workers. Those that do account for more than 50% of all production. The three major contracting organisations are:

> Soares da Costa
> Mota and Ca
> Construcões do Tamega

Other major contractors include Teixeira Duarte, Contrucões Technica, Somec and Elidio Monteiro. The contractors tend to be diverse in their activities, ranging from civil engineering (water, power and transport projects) to building works. Many have overseas contracts in the former colonies.

Portuguese contractors require a licence (*alvara*) to operate which is issued by the government. It is usually based on the company's technical and financial capacity. All work over 4 million escudos (£15 000) on government projects has to be undertaken by builders who hold a licence. There are six categories of licence that a contractor may hold which are given in terms of the size of contract (in contos, 1 conto = 1000 escudos). The licence bands are as follows:

> Up to C15 000   Up to C100 000
> Up to C25 000   Up to C200 000
> Up to C50 000   Up to C500 000

A number of foreign firms have gained a foothold in Portugal by merging with Portuguese contractors. British companies often undertake joint venture projects with Portuguese contractors on major villa development projects; for example, Bovis and Trafalgar House developments in the Algarve.

6.4 Extent of regionalisation

Geographically, Portugal comprises three main areas. These include the Algarve in the south, Lisbon in the central region and Porto in the north. Tourism is concentrated in the Algarve area and to the west of Lisbon around Estoril and Cascais.

An unpublished report prepared by J.Renda, entitled *Types of Traditional Building in Portugal* divides the country into six regions relative to building methods. Figure 6.1 indicates the division of the country into various named zones.

ZONES OR REGIONS OF TRADITIONAL BUILDING TYPES

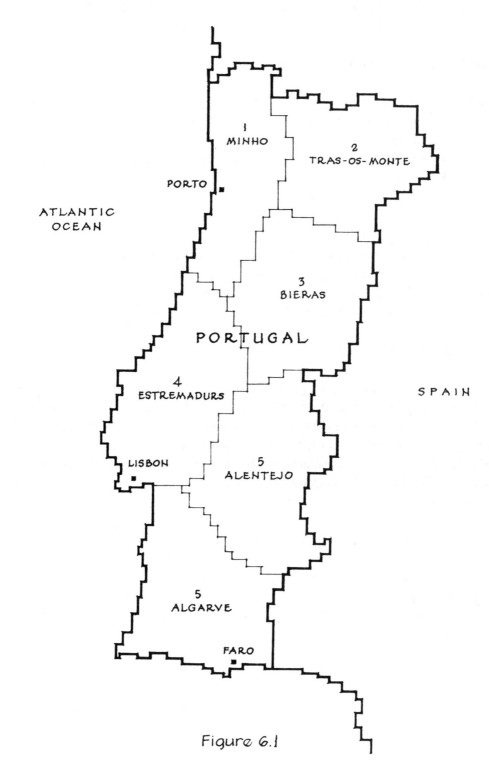

Figure 6.1

The report relates to the historic background relative to forms of building construction within each zone. Building methods have been directly influenced by climate, material resources and the need to provide shelter. A review of the building characteristics within each zone is outlined.

Zone 1 Minho, Litoral Duoro and Litoral Beira Regions

Simple domestic dwellings are constructed with granite or schist wall. Simple gabled roofs are of locally grown pine covered with clay tiles. Houses are two storeys in height with living accommodation on the first floor and accommodation for stables, cattle and storerooms on the ground floor. Figure 6.2 illustrates a diagrammatic front elevation and the floor plan at ground and first floor levels.

Zone 2 Tras-os-Montes and High Douro Region

Terraced two storey houses are constructed to form simple village street layouts. Stone built houses use local schist dry stone walling construction. Externally, the walls may be rendered and thin plates of schist applied as an external facing material. Sloping timber roofs are finished in locally made tiles.

Zone 3 Beiras Region

This is a mainly mountainous region in the centre of Portugal where local granite is used for the external wall construction. The surface of the stone is left exposed to form a natural finish. Floor and roof construction consists of local chestnut and pine timber joists covered with stone slabs to form the roof. Houses have characteristic heavy stone sills, heads and jambs to both external doors and windows. Figure 6.3 illustrates a layout of the ground and first floors of a typical village house also showing an elevation of the window and door features.

Zone 4 Estremadura, Ribatejo and Litoral Beira Regions

This region includes Lisbon and its extensive suburbs which contain modern buildings using up-to-date construction techniques. Similar techniques to those used on coastal villa and holiday developments in the Algarve region are used, that is, the use of reinforced concrete frames and terracotta block infill.

Within the rural regions a variety of building techniques are used. These include single storey timber houses constructed on raised timber piles.

TYPICAL HOUSE IN THE MINHO REGION - ZONE 1

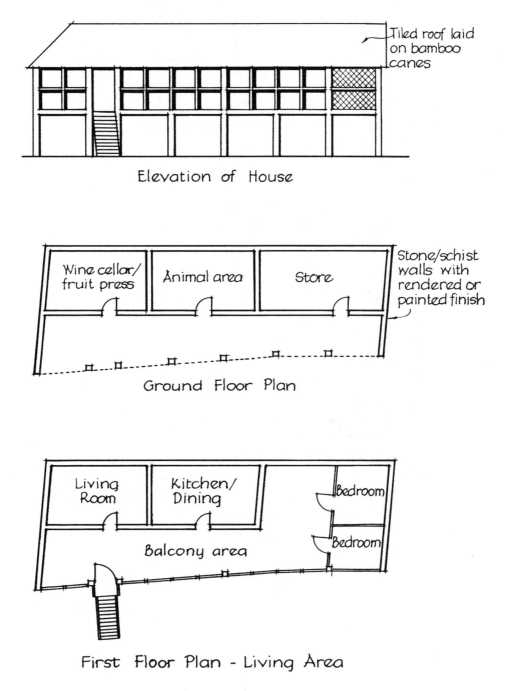

Tiled roof laid on bamboo canes

Elevation of House

Stone/schist walls with rendered or painted finish

Wine cellar/fruit press | Animal area | Store

Ground Floor Plan

Living Room | Kitchen/Dining | Bedroom

Balcony area | Bedroom

First Floor Plan - Living Area

Figure 6.2

TYPICAL DWELLING IN THE BEIRAS REGION - ZONE 3

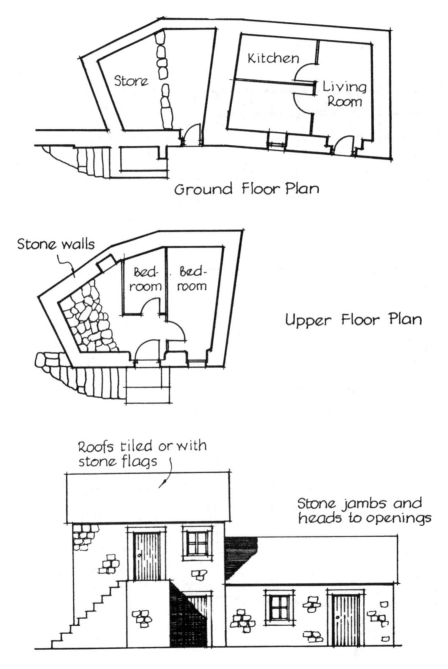

Ground Floor Plan

Upper Floor Plan

Elevation

Figure 6.3

External walls may also be constructed of locally made mud and straw building blocks. The external wall surface is rendered in a lime mortar and painted white on completion. Older traditional houses are single storey with sloping tiled roofs. Locally grown bamboo or canes are laid over the roofjoists prior to setting the tiles in cement mortar.

Zone 5 Alentejo Region

This again is a mountainous region of the country with villages constructed on terraced hillsides. Materials for external wall construction may be of locally made bricks or 'taipa' – mud walls consisting of sand, crushed stone and clay. The layout of the houses is of simple rectangular form. Counterfort walls are a common feature incorporated on the gable walls of buildings. Roof construction is of a brick vaulted type or flat roof.

Zone 6 Algarve, Low Alentejo and Litoral Alentejo Regions

Building techniques are influenced by demand the for housing, especially in the coastal tourist areas. Villa developments, single and terraced units, are constructed of reinforced concrete frames infilled with clay terracotta blocks. Medium rise flat developments are again constructed of reinforced concrete frames incorporating in situ or precast beam and block floors. Roofs may be flat or sloping and may be formed with timber or concrete units which are then tiled.

Houses in the country and rural areas are simple in layout and are constructed of stone or terracotta blocks maufactured locally. Extensive quantities of clay are available within the region for the manufacture of clay walling blocks, roof tiles and ceramic floor and wall tiles. In the mountain regions external walls may be constructed of local limestone or schist bonded with 'taipa' mud and straw.

Owing to the excellent Mediterranean climate houses incorporate patio and yard areas where one can dry fruits or the occupants can simply relax in the sun.

6.5 The housebuilding industry

In Portugal, housing is linked to commercial development in the inner city areas. In the Lisbon area, planners tend to favour developments of mixed commercial and residential use.

Credit restrictions and a lack of capital investment is limiting the construction of new accommodation for sale. Strict laws discourage the provision of accommodation to rent. Rental laws, which tend to protect existing tenants and limit rent increases, are currently under review.

Government estimates indicate that up to 5 million people live in substandard accommodation which lacks basic amenities. A further 135 000 people live in shanty towns on the edge of the larger cities.

Tourism and leisure development in the Algarve represents 30% of foreign investment which is currently being affected by the downturn in construction activity owing to the world recession. Some areas of the Algarve are overdeveloped and a number of completed development projects remain unsold.

Successful developments undertaken over the past ten years include Vilamoura, Vale do Lobo and Quinta do Largo. These tourist areas have been extended and have attracted clients working on joint venture projects. UK companies involved include Trafalgar House, Bovis Abroad Ltd and Emmerson Holdings. Case studies on villa developments are included in section 6.12.

6.6 Relationships within the construction industry

The engineer has been the dominant profession in Portugal for many years due to his involvement with the design and supervision aspects of projects. Since 1988, however, the professional competence between the architect and the engineer has been redefined to allow the architect to undertake a greater role in project design and supervision.

The relationship between the parties involved in the design and construction of a hotel-apartment project for a private owner is shown in figure 6.4. Due to the nature to the nature of the industry the majority of the work is undertaken by sub-contract labour or bona-fide sub-contracting firms. Local sub-contractors may be engaged on a competitive tendering basis to undertake the foundation works, frame and external infill blockwork. Specialist national contractors would be engaged for the specialist services work including building services, ventilation and air-conditioning installation.

RELATIONSHIP BETWEEN THE PARTIES

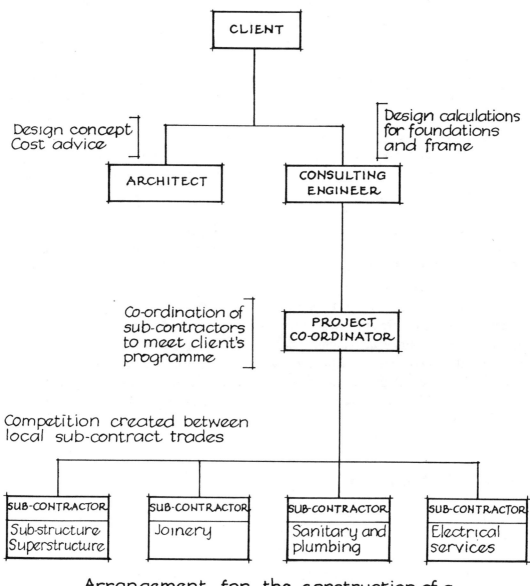

CLIENT

Design concept
Cost advice

Design calculations
for foundations
and frame

ARCHITECT

CONSULTING
ENGINEER

Co-ordination of
sub-contractors
to meet client's
programme

PROJECT
CO-ORDINATOR

Competition created between
local sub-contract trades

SUB-CONTRACTOR	SUB-CONTRACTOR	SUB-CONTRACTOR	SUB-CONTRACTOR
Sub-structure Superstructure	Joinery	Sanitary and plumbing	Electrical services

Arrangement for the construction of a
hotel / apartment project

Figure 6.4

6.7 Role of the architect

Architects undertake a five-year course at a recognised university in order to qualify as an architect. In 1988 a government decree was issued which redefined the role of the architect by indicating the type of projects which can be undertaken exclusively by architects (design work relative to conservation work, national monuments and classified historical areas including renovation of historical buildings). The decree also redefined the lines of professional competence between the architect and the engineer. Decree 465/88 assisted in laying down a new code of professional conduct and established the Association of Architects.

All Portuguese architects who provide services in Portugal and all European Community architects resident in the country must be members of the Association of Portuguese Architects. The Association will admit non-Portuguese architects who are qualified in accordance with EC directives subject to proof of experience. They must then register with the local council in whose area they intend to practice. The majority of the architects practice as individuals, with a small number of larger practices employing up to ten architects.

The main role of the architect is in the design aspects of buildings and the obtaining of planning permission for the proposed works. The responsibility for the site supervision is mainly undertaken by engineers or technical engineers. On certain projects the detail design may be undertaken by the contractors.

In general, projects may be designed and warranted by either engineers or architects. At the planning stage of a project architects must mediate with the authorities regarding new buildings or alteration projects which involve aesthetic changes. Architects may not carry out in structural calculations except in simple cases. Other more complicated structural calculations fall under the jurisdiction of a competent engineer.

On speculative developments many developer clients are unable to appoint an architect because of a lack of financial resources. In such cases the building design may be undertaken by the engineer.

6.8 Role of the engineer

The engineer has for many years been the dominant profession in Portugal. There are two types of qualified engineer:

1. University-trained engineers undertake a five-year degree course. Training at university is of an academic nature with the engineer specialising in an aspect of either structural engineering, hydraulics or urban planning (roads and bridges).

2. Technically trained engineers undertake a three-year course at a polytechnic. The technical engineer's education is more broadly based and less theoretical than that of his university counterpart. Emphasis is on the construction and management aspects of engineering and building projects.

On completion of a degree course, graduates are encouraged to join the Association of Graduate Engineers. When an engineer from a foreign country wishes to work in Portugal, the Ministry of Education liaises with the university at which the person qualified in order to confirm recognition of their diploma or degree award.

Engineers are involved in the design, quantification, administration and co-ordination of projects. Building developers often appoint a team of professional and technical engineers who are responsible for the financial and quality control aspects of a contract. The team has a role similar to that of the quantity surveyor and is made up of engineers who specialise in the cost and management aspects of construction projects.

Engineers may also be engaged by the contractor to undertake the role of the project manager. Project managers tend to specialise in the dimensional control and the supervision of projects. Buildings must be designed to withstand earthquake loadings and engineers are responsible for meeting the design criterion.

A Portuguese Association of Consulting Engineers and Management Consultants has been created, which is mainly supported by the medium and larger sized consulting organisations.

No qualifications are required for contractors to become civil engineering contractors (*constructoras civis*); however, contractors need to employ a qualified engineer in order to sign project documents.

Technical engineers

Technical engineers may undertake design work for buildings up to four storeys in height with a maximum cubic capacity of 800 cubic metres.

They may also undertake supervision and check quality control standards on construction projects. In practice they are more often employed by contractors than by consulting engineering practices.

6.9 Role of the quantity surveyor

The quantity surveying profession does not exist in Portugal. The role of the surveyor in the valuation process and in the agreement of final accounts is undertaken by the professional engineer or technical engineer who form part of the client's team.

A developer often appoints a team of engineers and technicians and other consultants (fiscals) on a building project who are responsible for the financial and quality control aspects of the project. The team has a similar role to that of the quantity surveyor and is made up of engineers who have specialised in this aspect of the construction process.

6.10 Contractual arrangements and building procurement

Procedures for building procurement and the relative tendering arrangements are different for public works and private works.

6.10.1 Normal procedures for public works

The arrangement applies to the smaller public works contracts which are considered of a straightforward nature. Contractors may compete as long as they have the technical and financial capabilities required by the tender conditions. They must be bonafide contractors and hold an official government licence in accordance with the classifications outlined in section 6.3.

Quantities are normally provided as part of the tender documentation. Price is considered the deciding factor, as all contractors tendering are assumed to be of the same technical and managerial standing.

Contractors may also be required to tender on the basis of a specification and drawings. In these cases the contractor is responsible for the assessment of his own quantities

A tender submission may be submitted by a group of firms with one acting as main contractor.

6.10.2 Pre-qualification procedures for public works

The government has passed legislation to control the construction of large buildings and complex projects for which pre-qualification tenders are required from firms that wish to compete. These firms may form consortia, joint ventures or 'Associations of Companies' (ACE) to enable them to carry out the works. Tender conditions or pre-qualifications may be concerned with aspects of the companies technical ability, financial status, quality and maintenance of the finished product. The company will have to provide evidence of a proven track record on similar types of projects and clearly demonstrate that the materials and equipment involved in the construction will satisfy the client's needs.

Based on the pre-qualification requirements, a short list of five or six builders or consortiums will be selected to submit a bid.

Proposals must follow procedure laid down in decree 348-A/86 and 605A-B-C/V86 and the conditions outlined in the tender documents.

All documents are presented in a series of different envelopes, and at each stage in the process the conditions of tendering are strictly enforced.

Envelope one contains:	qualification requirements.
Envelope two contains:	specification of materials and equipment.
Envelope three contains:	unit prices of materials and specifications of equipment that the builder proposes to use.
Envelope four contains:	conditions which are relevant to the contractors bid.

6.10.3 Private contract arrangements

Standard forms of contract for private works do not exist in Portugal and many contract forms follow the public works system.

The main contractor is usually a civil engineering firm that puts together the bid which will include the specialist work of electrical and mechanical sub-contractors. In most contracts each specialist sub-contractor will present his own price proposals. The main contractor is entitled to add a percentage addition to the sub-contractor's quotation in order to cover for project co-ordination, supervision and the programming of the works.

When large contracts are let they are often undertaken by a consortium of contractors which include all the specialist trades. In this case the separate trade arrangements (*lots separais*) similar to the French system are used.

There is then no main contractor since all sub-contractors have a direct contract with the client. This necessitates a large team of professionals (the fiscals) to deal with client liaison, co-ordination, supervision and control of the project.

6.11 Planning and building control procedures

Portugal is divided into approximately three hundred and twenty municipalities which are responsible for planning permission. Decree 166/70 regulates the procedures for obtaining planning permission which is only applicable to private works. Buildings of public works needs no authorisation from the municipal authorities.

Planning permission is needed for most of private construction work including rebuilding, extensions, restoration or the demolition of buildings. Exceptions are made for maintenance or conversion work which only involve minor modifications.

Procedures for obtaining a building permit depend upon the nature of the project and can be categorised into 'small' projects, 'large' projects and tourist projects.

In the case of 'small' and 'large' projects, building proposals are submitted to the local authority. Within each local authority the proposals are then circulated to the planning, architectural, technical services and health departments. After consideration, the proposals are returned to the architect outlining any amendments which must be met. The architect will then be required to resubmit the applications, together with a declaration that the construction meets the appropriate building standards. Once this is found to be satisfactory, a building permit will be granted.

Small projects are dealt with by the planning, architectural, technical and health departments of the local authority (*camara*).

Large projects involve similar local authority scrutiny and will require additional approval from the regional planning authorities and specific ministry department.

Tourist projects (hotel complexes and residential developments in tourist areas like the Algarve), require an application to be made directly to the Ministry of Tourism. After consideration of the proposals the local authority is consulted for an opinion.

Building regulations and technical control

Architects and engineers have a number of regulations to comply with in terms of safety and the correct use of materials. Provisions dealing with building regulations and control are set out in decree 718/87. This gives a detailed list of all legal measures and technical responsibility of the architect and engineer.

Technical control of construction work is carried out by the municipalities. During the execution of work inspections are made on site by a technical inspector or the municipal authority at two stages of the work.

Stage one inspections are undertaken at the excavation of foundation stage. The second inspection takes place on completion of the foundations. On completion of the works an occupation licence will be issued.

Observations of quality control standards on speculative villa developments in the Algarve

Once the contract commences the building contractor tends to have a 'free-hand' regarding building method, quality control and safety procedures.

Formwork techniques used for the frame construction leave much to be desired. It is evident that extensive use is made of sub-contract labour including 'specialist gangs' for the erection of formwork and reinforcement. Traditional board formwork is mainly used which quickly deteriorates with extensive remaking and reuse. Formwork support systems appear visually unsafe and inadequate, with little use of steel scaffolding.

The finished concrete is often honeycombed, poorly compacted at wall and column kicker levels and the ill-fitting formwork leaks extensively. Vertical and horizontal alignment problems are also evident.

The positioning and cover to steel reinforcement for reinforced concrete staircases are frequently unsatisfactory. The surface finish to treads and landings is poor. Extensive gaps are often evident between brickwork infill panels and the soffits of the beams in the concrete frames. The contractor's attitude appears to be that 'the cement rendering process will ultimately cover up all the workmanship defects between the frame and brickwork' – and so it does.

This has resulted in extensive cracking appearing in the external rendering. Evidence of extensive repair work can be readily observed on completed villas on many developments in the Algarve.

There is obviously a need for clients to apply a system of quality inspection checks during construction. Quality control and workmanship on speculative developments is often overlooked in times of rapid development expansion. There is no equivalent of BS 5756 in Portugal.

Similar problems relating to the quality control of the concrete frame and cladding have also been observed in other Mediterranean areas, i.e. Cyprus, the Greek mainland and islands, and the Spanish islands.

6.12 Low rise housing construction

Information collection

The case study material relates to a number of villa and residential flat development projects in the Algarve region of Portugal.

Data relating to construction techniques has been obtained from visiting developments areas, developers and building contractors in the Faro area The construction techniques dealt with may not be typical of building methods used in other regions.

6.12.1 Form of construction

Low rise building techniques for social housing and villa development utilise in situ concrete framed construction for the main building frame.

The building must be designed by an engineer in order to resist collapse by earthquake; hence the extensive use of in situ concrete framed buildings to provide structural continuity.

Foundation bases are tied together by a series of interconnecting ground beams. In situ concrete suspended floors and roofs are used. Precast beam and block floor construction incorporates in situ concrete tie beams to provide structural continuity. Structural timber, however, appears to be in short supply and precast beam and block construction may also be used to form low pitched roofs. Roof slopes are battened and tiled using locally made clay pantiles.

Externally the concrete frame is infilled with terracotta block walls which are rendered externally and plaster finished internally. External features are made of in situ columns to form archways, barbecue areas and covered patios where the residents can relax in the temperate climate. Sun terraces are often formed on roof areas with external stair access from gardened or patio areas. External or internal window shutters are provided as a additional means of security. Houses are externally rendered and finished with white painted surfaces and capped with the traditional Algarvian chimneys.

Maximum use is made of the natural building materials available in the region i.e. aggregates for concrete, clay for block walls and local stone for feature walls. Locally manufactured ceramic tiles are extensively used for ground and first floor areas.

A range of typical Algarvian villa designs is illustrated in figure 6.5.

6.13 Case study – low rise housing construction

6.13.1 Development layout

Figures 6.6 and 6.7 illustrate the layout plans of two speculative development projects. Extensive features are made of the natural landscape of pine forests, and the construction of a man-made lake. Developments incorporate landscaped areas and swimming pool facilities to service the residents.

A selection of typical Algarvian chimney features are shown in figure 6.7. The floor plans for a three-storey linked villa are shown in figure 6.8.

LOW RISE HOUSING / VILLA DESIGNS

Linked Villas

Detached Villas

Terraced Villas

Figure 6.5

LOW RISE HOUSING / VILLA LAYOUT

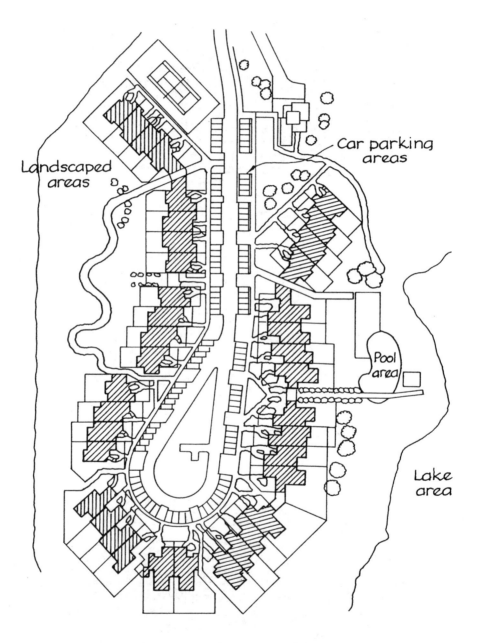

Development layout plan

Figure 6.6

6.13.2 Foundation element

Figure 6.9 illustrates the foundation ground beam and the column layouts for a small detached villa. A series of interconnecting ground beams provides lateral ties to the ground floor area and aids the layout of the precast floor units. Ground floor construction is of the prestressed beam and infill block type. On completion of the frame and blockwork infill the floor units are screeded and ceramic tiled.

6.13.3 Structural concrete frame

The building frame may be constructed first followed by the infill blockwork – figure 6.10, Detail A. This is the procedure adopted in the majority of situations. However, some alternative methods of constructing the blockwork and frame as a combined operation have been developed in Portugal. The sequence of construction is illustrated in figure 6.10 Details B and C. Using this sequence of construction the blockwork acts as the formwork on two sides of the column and on the suspended beam soffit.

Quality control regarding the positioning and spacing of the reinforcement appears suspect. Dimensional control and the stability of the formwork during compaction of the concrete also requires close scrutiny.

In order to provide structural continuity between the precast floors and the in situ frame, in situ concrete strip beams are incorporated in the floor construction. The in situ beams are constructed at right angles to the span of the precast concrete floor beams as shown in figure 6.11.

6.13.4 External and internal wall construction

External wall construction, forming the infill wall to the concrete frame, consists of two 100 mm or 125 mm terracotta block walls. The 25 mm cavity is filled with polystyrene sheet insulation positioned during the wall construction. Externally the wall surface is cement rendered (figure 6.12, Detail A).

As an alternative the external wall may be constructed of a 200 mm single block wall to form the external envelope (detail B). Internal walls are formed of 75 mm or 100 mm terracotta blocks which are plaster finished to both sides (detail C). Detail D illustrates a section through the external wall and floors of a low rise building. Problems of internal condensation due to cold bridging at lintels are apparent in the external wall detail over the the window heads.

LOW RISE HOUSING / VILLA LAYOUT

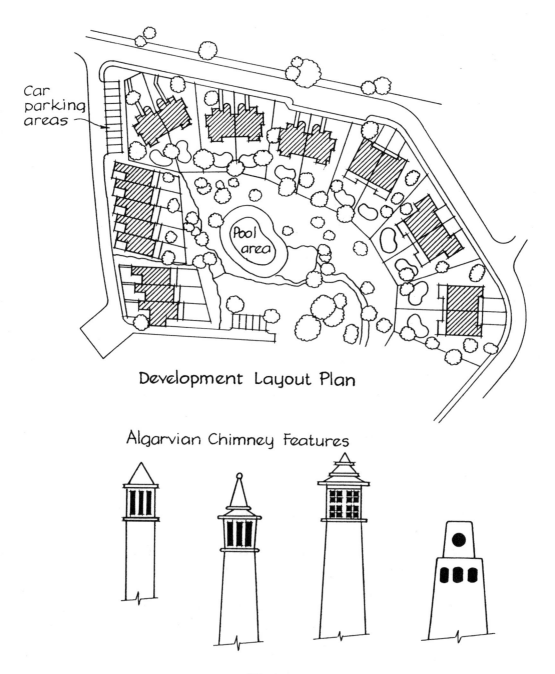

Car parking areas

Pool area

Development Layout Plan

Algarvian Chimney Features

Figure 6.7

LOW RISE HOUSING / VILLA LAYOUT

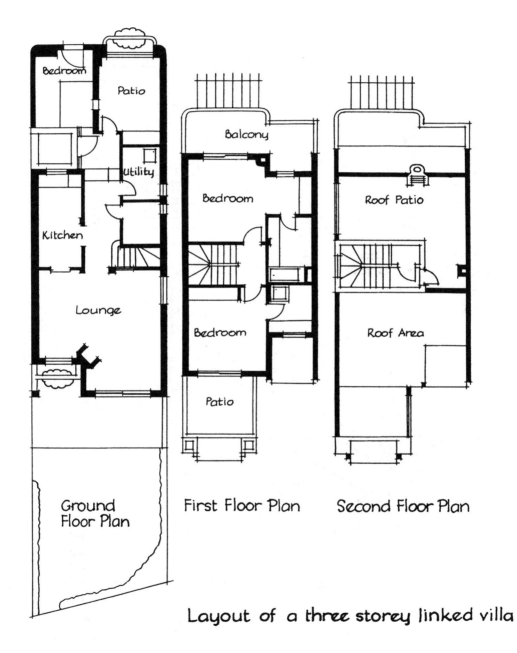

Ground
Floor Plan

First Floor Plan

Second Floor Plan

Layout of a three storey linked villa

Figure 6.8

FOUNDATION CONSTRUCTION

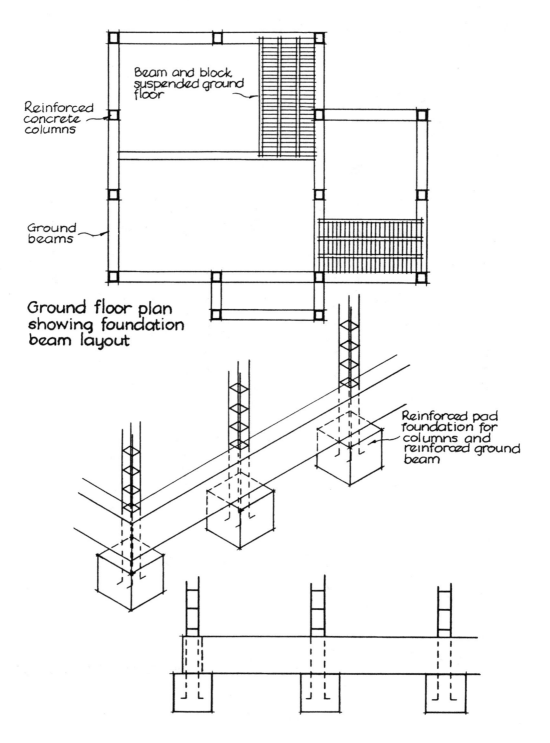

Beam and block suspended ground floor

Reinforced concrete columns

Ground beams

Ground floor plan showing foundation beam layout

Reinforced pad foundation for columns and reinforced ground beam

Figure 6.9

FRAME CONSTRUCTION

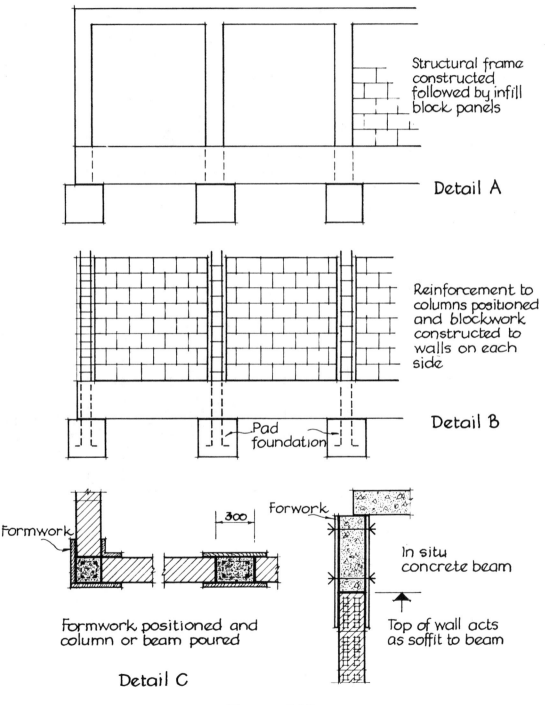

Structural frame constructed followed by infill block panels

Detail A

Reinforcement to columns positioned and blockwork constructed to walls on each side

Pad foundation

Detail B

Formwork

300

Formwork

In situ concrete beam

Top of wall acts as soffit to beam

Formwork positioned and column or beam poured

Detail C

Figure 6.10

FLOOR CONSTRUCTION

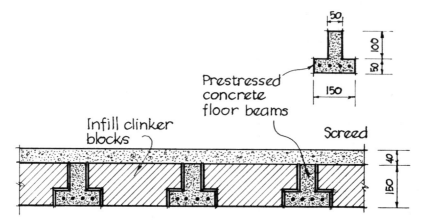

Ground Floor Construction

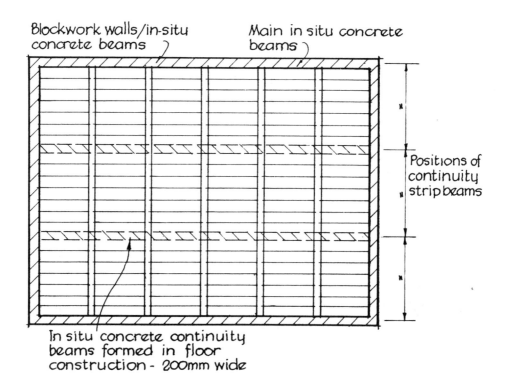

First Floor Construction

Figure 6.11

6.13.5 Roof construction

Roofs are of a shallow pitch and usually finished in red terracotta clay tiles. The structural roof is constructed of in situ concrete or alternatively of the prestressed beam and infill block type as shown in figure 6.13.

In situ roof construction will incorporate an in situ concrete ridge beam, and in situ concrete gutters. The concrete surface is then battened to receive clay tiles.

Small feature roofs and entrance canopies may be constructed of timber rafters and purlins. The use of traditional timber roof construction is not common on villa developments owing to the shortage of structural timber materials.

6.13.6 Use of natural material resources within the Mediterranean countries

All the Mediterranean countries make full use of the natural building material sources within each region. In Portugal, Spain, France, and Greece modern construction techniques have developed around the use of concrete, as each region normally has a natural supply of aggregates. Imported cement is cheap and is obtained from many sources.

Clay and concrete block making plants and precast concrete supplies abound, to serve the needs of the developers and speculators.

6.14 Medium rise construction

Form of construction

Medium rise residential developments in the private sector (villa projects over two storeys in height) or those used for inner city flat developments are constructed of in situ reinforced concrete frames. The foundation to the frames consists of large pad foundations bearing on rock; alternatively piled foundations may be used.

The frame is normally constructed on a square or rectangular grid layout to suit the building plan dimensions. In situ concrete downstand beams support in situ floors or precast beam and block floors. The concrete frame externally is infilled with terracotta blocks to form the external envelope which is then rendered.

Aspects of construction safety and temporary works considerations leave much to be desired. The implications of EU regulations will take a long time to have an impact at site construction level – if at all.

EXTERNAL WALL CONSTRUCTION

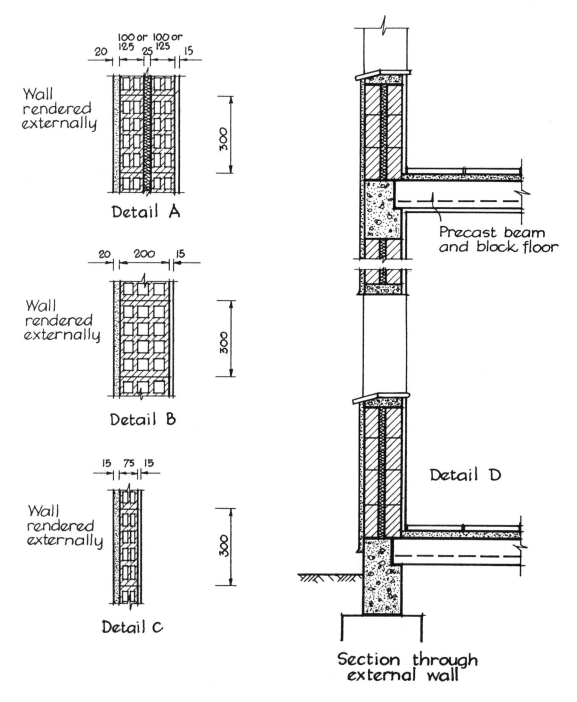

100 or 100 or
20   125   25   125   15

Wall
rendered
externally

300

Detail A

20   200   15

Wall
rendered
externally

300

Detail B

15   75   15

Wall
rendered
externally

300

Detail C

Precast beam
and block floor

Detail D

Section through
external wall

Figure 6.12

ROOF CONSTRUCTION

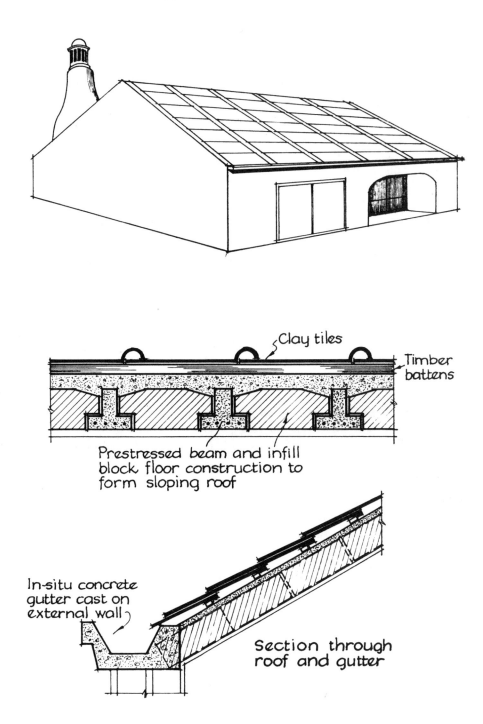

Clay tiles

Timber battens

Prestressed beam and infill block floor construction to form sloping roof

In-situ concrete gutter cast on external wall

Section through roof and gutter

Figure 6.13

7 Comparative Data in the European Union

The following data relating to other European Countries may be of interest for comparison with the data given for the countries covered in the main text.

Section

Section 1 United Kingdom

Key information

Capital – London
Area (sq. km) 229 880   Population 53.92m (1991)

Construction output (1990)

Data obtained from Euroconstruct Conference Report June 1991

	ECU Billion	Pounds Billion
New residential construction	9.61	6.86
Private non-residential construction (offices, industrial and commercial)	18.86	13.47
Public non-residential construction (schools, universities, hospitals)	3.68	2.63
New civil engineering work	7.61	5.43
Renovation in civil engineering	2.83	2.02
Renovation and modernisation in residential property	14.97	10.69
Non-residential renovation	10.29	7.34
Total	67.84 ECU	£48.44

Conversion rate 1 ECU = £0.741

Section 2 Belgium

Key information

Capital Brussels
Area (sq. km) 30 518   Population 10.02m (1992)

Construction output (1990)

Data obtained from Euroconstruct Conference Report – June 1991

	ECU Billion
New residential construction	7.6
Private non-residential construction (offices, industrial and commercial)	6.25
Public non-residential construction (schools, universities, hospitals)	1.0
New civil engineering work	
Renovation in civil engineering	1.62
Renovation and modernisation in residential property	
Non-residential renovation	3.18
	————
Total	9.65 ECU

Conversion rate 1 ECU = 42.42 B Francs

Section 3 Ireland

Key information

Capital – Dublin
Area (sq. km) 70 282   Population 3.55m (1992)

Construction output (1990)

Data obtained from Euroconstruct Conference Report – June 1991

	ECU Billion
New residential construction	1.021
Private non-residential construction (offices, industrial and commercial)	0.738
Public non-residential construction (schools, universities, hospitals)	0.156
New civil engineering work	0.463
Renovation in civil engineering	0.233
Renovation and modernisation in residential property	0.519
Non-residential renovation	0.243
Total	**3.373 ECU**

Conversion rate 1 ECU = 0.768 Punts

Section 4 Italy

Key information

Capital – Rome
Area (sq. km) 301 302   Population 56.41m (1991)

Construction output (1990)

Data obtained from Euroconstruct Conference Report – June 1991

	ECU Billion
New residential construction	23.71
Private non-residential construction (offices, industrial and commercial)	14.12
Public non-residential construction (schools, universities, hospitals)	3.25
New civil engineering work	10.56
Renovation in civil engineering	6.47
Renovation and modernisation in residential property	20.56
Non-residential renovation	15.83
Total	94.50 ECU

Conversion rate 1 ECU = 1524.8 Lire

Section 6 Spain

Key information

Capital – Madrid
Area (sq. km) 492 592   Population 38.87m (1991)

Construction output (1990)

Data obtained from Euroconstruct Conference Report – June 1991

	ECU Billion
New residential construction	15.53
Private non-residential construction (offices, industrial and commercial)	5.90
Public non-residential construction (schools, universities, hospitals)	2.79
New civil engineering work	15.70
Renovation in civil engineering	4.42
Renovation and modernisation in residential property	3.03
Non-residential renovation	5.44
Total	52.81 ECU

Conversion rate 1 ECU = 129.6 Pesetas

Section 6 Exchange rates in ECUs

The following are average daily rates for 1991.

Country	1 ECU is equivalent to:	
Belgium	72.420	BEF (Belgian franc)
Denmark	7.870	DKK (Danish krone)
France	6.914	FRF (French franc)
Germany	1.955	DEM (Deutsche Mark)
Ireland	0.768	IEP (Irish punt)
Italy	1524.000	ITL (lira)
The Netherlands	2.320	NLG (guilder)
Portugal	180.000	PTE (escudo)
Spain	129.600	ESP (peseta)
United Kingdom	0.714	GBP (pound sterling)

Section 7 Percentage of home ownership in the EU countries

Percentages are shown in descending order.

Source – House Prices – *The Economist* 26 December 1992

Country	% home ownership
Ireland	82
Spain	80
Belgium	73
Greece	73
Italy	68
United Kingdom	66
Denmark	60
France	54
Holland	45
Germany	40

Section 8 Top twenty construction companies in Europe – 1991

Position	Company	Country	Turnover £m
1	Bouygues	France	6469
2	SGE	France	4493
3	BICC	United Kingdom	3790
4	Philipp Holzmann	Germany	3761
5	Iritecna	Italy	3702
6	Tarmac	United Kingdom	3225
7	Trafalgar House	United Kingdom	3202
8	Skanska	Sweden	3140
9	SAE	France	2740
10	GTM Entrepose	France	2704
11	AMEC	United Kingdom	2338
12	Hochtief	Germany	2200
13	Spie Batignolles	France	2170
14	NBC	Sweden	2017
15	Beazer	United Kingdom	1927
16	Bllfinger & Berger	Germany	1807
17	George Wimpey	United Kingdom	1753
18	Dumez	France	1698
19	Cegelee	France	1600
20	John Laing	United Kingdom	1586

Source – Fransen Domineren De Europese Bouwmarket, 4 December 1991

References and Bibliography

Denmark

'Development - housing in Denmark', The Ministry of Housing, 1990. (This is an overview of recent trends with examples of completed experimental building projects, published as a brochure by The National Building and Housing Agency.)
AB 1992 The Danish Building Contract, Danish Ministry of Housing.

France

Technologie Du Batiment - Gros Oeuvre, Ouvrager En Béton Armé, H. Renaud and F. Laterie, Les Editions Foucher, Paris, 1978.

Constructeur Bâtiment Technologie I & II, H. Renaud, Les Éditions Foucher, Paris, 1985.

The French Construction Industry - A guide for UK professionals, CIRIA, Special Publication 65, 1989.

'French leave - A manager's guide to French construction', M. Shallon, *Chartered Builder*, December 1992.

'The Business of Building in France', Joint RICS/Chambre de Commerce Française de Grande-Bretagne. Published 1993 in association with the Royal Institution of Chartered Surveyors.

'French Lessons', D. Cartlidge, *New Builder*, 5 February 1993.

Germany

The West German Construction Industry - A guide for UK professionals, CIRIA Special Publication 68, 1990.

'European Outlook - Germany and Belgium', J. Collinge, *Architects Journal*, 20 March 1991.

'Making a Mark', *New Builder*, 14 November 1991.

The Netherlands

'The hook of Holland - UK architects find a niche', M. Spring and G. Ridout, *Building*, 29 January 1993.

Portugal

The Iberian Construction Industries - A guide for UK professionals, CIRIA Special Publication 67, 1982.

Special report on Portugal, G. Graham, *Financial Times,* 3 April 1989.

'European Outlook - Spain, Portugal, France', *Architects Journal,* 20 February 1991.

'Types of traditional buildings in Portugal', Instituto Politecnico de Faro - Engo Jorge Renda. Special report for a visiting lecture programme.

European Union (other countries)

The Italian Construction Industry - A guide for UK Professionals, CIRIA Special Publication 76, 1990.

The Construction Industry and the European Community, N.F. Spencer Chapman and C. Grandjean, Blackwell Scientific Publications, 1991.

'Breaking down the barriers in Europe', 1992. Special report by Phillips and Drew.

'Planning in Europe', The Royal Town Planning Institute, 1993. A series of tapes which provide a basic introduction to planning procedures in Italy, Spain, France, Germany, The Netherlands and Europe.

'Construction Research and Development - A comparative review of four countries', The Chartered Institute of Building (covers a review of research and development in Federal Germany, France, Japan and the USA).

'The Euro Pioneers', M. Pettipher, *New Builder*, 11 July 1991.

'European Outlook - Italy and Greece', J. Collinge, *Architects Journal,* 4 September 1991.

'EC Directives and the Workplace', *The Building Surveyor*, May 1992.

'Directive Update', *Chartered Builder*, November 1992.

'House Prices', *The Economist*, Issue 26, December 1992-8 January 1993.

'Procurement European Costings', *Building,* Issue 22, January 1993.

'European Community - Measures affecting professional practice', M. Ankers, *Chartered Builder*, June 1993.

'Procurement European Costings', *Building*, Issue 25 March 1994

General

The European Community, A Guide to the Maze, Stanley A. Budd and Alun Jones, Kogan Page, 1987.

Building Control - Europe 1992 - Proceedings National Building Control Conference June 1989.

'Selling to Europe - A country by country guide to public sector purchasing', NEDO Publication, 1990.

'Gateway to Europe - a manual for the construction industry', NEDC Publication, 1990.

'A Community of Twelve: Key Figures', Commission of the European Communities, 1991.

Guide to 1992: Explanation of the Free European Market Northcote Associates, ISBN 18 712 5500 7

Europe in Ten Lessons, Pascal Fontaine, Office of Official Publications of the European Communities, 1992.

'Who decides what in the European Community. A brief guide to policy making in the EEC', UK Office of the Commission, March 1993.

'Euronews Construction', Department of Environment and Building.

Euroconstruct. Contact address for economic data on EU countries: Economisch Instituut voor de Bouwnijverheid, De Cuserstraat 89, 1081 CN, Amsterdam.